THE TWELVE CORE ACTION VALUES

Workbook for the Values Coach Guided Self-Coaching Course

Created by JOE TYE, Head Coach, Values Coach America

Dedication

For Sally. Happiness is being married to your best friend.

Table of Contents

Introduction

A guide for making *The Twelve Core Action Values* your roadmap to a rich and rewarding life

I know something about you, something you might not even know about yourself: You have good solid values. You intuitively know the right thing to do in most situations, and you want to be able to take pride in who you are and what you do. If you're like almost everyone else in this world, here's something else I know about you: You haven't really taken the time to specify what your core values are, much less the actions you can take to do a better job of living those values. You haven't seriously reflected upon how those values should be reflected in the goals you set and in the choices you make, nor have you thought about how you would make a decision in situations where you could honor one value but not another. Furthermore, if you're like virtually everyone else, there is a gap (perhaps a wide gap) between what you say your values are and what the proverbial Man from Mars would observe in your attitudes and in your behaviors.

If I've described your situation, I have good news for you: *The Twelve Core Action Values* are your values. I know that because these values are universal and eternal; they have been honored in each of the world's major cultures for thousands of years. It doesn't matter what your political affiliation, religious beliefs, or national heritage is: *these are your values.* By the time we complete this course, you will agree with that statement. Before we began, let's define what we mean by "values," a term that has been greatly misused in recent years. True values run much deeper than cultural traditions, political slogans, or business goals. Here's my definition:

> *Core Value (noun):*
>
> *A deeply-internalized philosophical guide that profoundly influences goal-setting, decision-making, conflict resolution, and more generally how one lives one's life.*

For this course, we will be adding the word "action" to this definition: unless values are acted upon, they are nothing more than good intentions. In recent years, we've seen too many examples in the worlds of business, politics, and religion of people talking a good talk about their values, but then failing to act upon them, often to the detriment of their organizations and to the people who have trusted in their leadership. Action is the distinction between good intentions and real contributions.

Action (verb)

The process of exerting energy (emotional and physical) directed toward the accomplishment of a desired change or goal.

For each of *The Twelve Core Action Values* there are four cornerstones. This is how we put action into those values, making them real in our attitudes and in our behaviors. This study guide will give you practical and proven ideas and strategies for living your values. And it comes with this promise: the more conscientious you are about living these values, the more successful you will be at achieving your most important goals, and the happier and more fulfilled you will be as a human being.

Before we get started, let me warn you that this course does not prescribe an easy "silver bullet" path to instant success and infinite wealth. Quite to the contrary, the journey will be tough and demanding. It will require hard work on your part. You'll be challenged mentally, emotionally, and spiritually. You will make incredible progress one day, only to be discouraged by finding yourself backsliding the next day. You'll be tempted to quit, probably more than once. Be ready for all of these things—they are just part of the process. Your frustration will not kill you, it will make you stronger.

There's something else you need to be ready for. What you learn through this course, if you take it seriously, might scare you. Introspection can always be frightening, and this course demands lots of introspection. The most frightening thing of all might be when the "you" of today comes face-to-face with the "you" that could be, the "you" that you are meant to be. We'll be taking the basket off a candle that you've carefully kept covered up all these years, and exposing the incredible potential of that shining inner light of yours. When the "you who is" comes face-to face with the "you who could be," it can be intimidating, so prepare yourself now to confront that fear with courage and determination. It can also be liberating and exhilarating.

The structure of this curriculum

Each of the 60 modules in this study guide will follow a consistent format. First we'll outline our goal for that module, and illustrate it with a short story or anecdote. Then I'll share essential ideas and actions for living that value, plus several Rules for the Journey. We'll conclude with a take-home exercise and a suggestion for further reading. Here is an outline of the anatomy of the course—the continuum that links the process of internalizing and operationalizing your values with the achievement of your goals in the real world:

Core Values

The **why** that motivates personal transformation and galvanizes action toward authentic dreams and goals.

Cornerstones

The **what** that makes core values become real by making them actionable and observable.

Action Steps

The **how** of achievement—without action, even the best of values are nothing more than good intentions.

Outcomes

The **where** of achievement, the new destination arrived at as a result of working with and living your values.

The power of *The Twelve Core Action Values* curriculum lies in this structure. Philosophy backed up by action, theory reinforced by experience. While the curriculum rests on a rock-solid theoretical foundation, the emphasis from start to finish will be on practical action strategies which at the end of the day will help you be more effective in just about every facet of your life and work. This course will help you make the changes in your beliefs, attitudes, and behaviors that are necessary for you to achieve your goals and your dreams. Here's a preview of the course outline, including some of the benefits you will realize for each value:

Core Action Values 1-6: Laying a Solid Foundation

Core Action Value #1: Authenticity

You will gain a greater sense of who you are, and of who you are meant to be; you will learn practical strategies to overcome the inner barriers that are holding you back, and to build the solid self-belief that is required for you to become that meant-to-be person.

Core Action Value #2: Integrity

To be considered a person of integrity is the highest honor. I'll share specific actions you can take so that you never become your own worst enemy, but rather earn the sense of pride (and the reputation) that come from knowing that you always do the right thing.

Core Action Value #3: Awareness

This is a foundation of both emotional intelligence and spiritual peace; you will learn disciplines that will help you enhance your ability to more accurately and objectively observe what's going on within you and around you.

Core Action Value #4: Courage

You will learn to identify the fears that are holding you back, how to make those fears work for you and not against you, and how to confront the dragon of fear with the sword of determination.

Core Action Value #5: Perseverance

You'll learn practical strategies to prepare for adversity, and for confronting the inevitable obstacles and setbacks with mental toughness and a positive perspective.

Core Action Value #6: Faith

Throughout history, faith has been the most powerful form of human motivation. I'll show you how, whatever your religious beliefs happen to be, you can reinforce the power of faith in yourself, in your future, and in a power that is beyond human sight.

Core Action Values 7-12: Taking Effective Action

Core Action Value #7: Purpose

You will discover a greater sense of purpose and meaning in the work you do, and learn practical skills for being a more positive contributor and team-builder in your organization.

Core Action Value #8: Vision

I'll share techniques for getting out of your box and re-sparking the incredible imagination you were born with; you'll learn a formula for transforming your dreams into *memories of the future.*

Core Action Value #9: Focus

The tools and techniques I'll share will help you conquer procrastination, fuel a powerful sense of urgency, and become more productive than you've ever been before.

Core Action Value #10: Enthusiasm

I'll show you how to tap into energy that you never suspected you had, and with this energy become more positive, more optimistic, and happier in virtually every dimension of your life.

Core Action Value #11: Service

It is an ancient paradox that those who are most committed to serving others end up being more successful themselves; I'll show you how this spirit of serving will help you achieve your personal and professional goals as you help others do the same.

Core Action Value #12: Leadership

To be a leader is not a job description, it is a way of looking at the world and an ongoing personal commitment to taking initiative to solve problems and create opportunities. In this final section, we'll cover actions you can take to be a more effective leader—in your family and in your community as well as at work.

Think of a rocket ship that's been launched toward the moon. If you alter its course by just one tiny degree as it is coming off the launch pad, it will miss the moon altogether and end up in the stars. In the same way, small changes that you make as a result of participating in this course, and which you sustain over a period of time, will have a huge impact upon your future success and happiness. Five or ten years from now, you will be in a much better place—professionally, personally, financially, spiritually, and in many other ways—than you would have been otherwise.

Personal values and organizational values

Most organizations have a formal statement of values. A values statement is a powerful way of publicly stating what the organization stands for (and what it won't stand for). Most organizational values statements include a blend of values, behaviors, and outcomes. For example, integrity is a core value; honesty and reliability are behaviors that reflect that underlying value; and trust is the outcome that's earned by being honest and reliable. Appreciating this continuum can help an organization's leaders gain buy-in to its corporate values, expectations, and goals. As an example, let's say an organization's goal is superior customer service. The required behaviors to achieve that goal include having people act in a positive and cheerful manner, and take a genuine interest in their customers. The underlying value that drives these behaviors is enthusiasm (Core Action Value #10) and its cornerstones of Attitude, Energy, Curiosity and Humor.

Beginning with the end in mind (as Stephen Covey reminds us to do in his 7 habits of highly effective people) means starting with the organization's goal, determining the behaviors required to achieve that goal, and then linking those behaviors to the underlying personal values. People are more likely to behave in the desired manner when they see it as being central to their core values than if they're just trying to please the boss.

The seven simple promises of *The Self-Empowerment Pledge*

To act upon the values we'll study in this course requires desire and initiative—which in turn requires that you become self-empowered. The truth of the matter is that no one can empower you but you. And once you have empowered yourself, no one can take that power away. The seven simple promises (simple, though not always easy) of *The Self-Empowerment Pledge* will help you to be more responsible, accountable, and determined; more committed to making a contribution and to bouncing back from every adversity; and more dedicated to maintaining a positive perspective and to letting your faith shine through in your attitudes and in your actions. That is a pretty good definition of the self-empowered person, isn't it?

Take a minute to read the seven promises of *The Pledge* on page 9. Then ask yourself these questions:

> *What if each member of your family were to take those promises to heart? Would you have a richer and more rewarding experience together? Would each family member be more likely to do their part (and to do their chores)? Would you be more supportive of each other within the family?*

> *And what about the place where you work? What if everyone made a good-faith effort to keep these seven simple promises? Would you do a better job of serving your customers, and of supporting each other?*

Here's another question: If you knew it would change your life profoundly and permanently for the better, would you invest 365 minutes in yourself over the next year—one minute a day, every day? (I know it's a big sacrifice—I'm asking you to give up watching one television commercial.) If your answer is yes, here's what you do: Monday morning you get up and recite to yourself Monday's Promise—and do it like you really mean it, with feeling and passion. Do it again at your lunch break, once more at the end of your working day, and one more time right before you go to bed. It takes about 15 seconds to say each promise, so four times a day is one minute. It also helps if you place visual cues where you'll see them often. Go to the *Pledge Power* website and print out as many mini-posters as you need. Put one up on the bathroom mirror, put one in your gym locker and post one in your work area; make the seven promises the daily screensaver on your computer; leave a copy on the seat of your car so you see it every time you open the door.

www.Pledge-Power.com

The promises themselves are simple, but keeping them will require desire and determination. Fortunately, you don't have to do it all at once. Focus on one promise each day, so that you make all seven promises to yourself each week. Do this each day for one year—it will be the best daily one minute that you will ever invest in yourself. For best results, make the promises while looking in the mirror at the beginning of the day. At first you might feel awkward. You might even feel like a bit of a fraud. But gradually, the words will start to sink in, begin to act upon your attitudes and beliefs. This will have a positive influence on your behaviors and actions, which will in turn begin to generate better outcomes, thus reinforcing your belief in the promise.

When you first start making these promises to yourself, please do not be surprised if you don't experience an immediate transformation (in fact, I'll be astonished if you *do* experience an immediate transformation!). In fact, you're more likely to hear the voice of negative self-talk telling you how ridiculous you are to be talking to yourself that way. Ignore that voice and keep saying the words. It will take a while for them to sink in. But if you keep saying the words, they will sink in. Say them enough and you'll learn them by heart. Think about those two words—*by heart*. The heart does not learn, that is the province of the head. To say that you have learned something "by heart" means you have internalized it at a deeper level than mere knowledge. The words have become a part of you.

Now begins the hard part. As the words start to sink in, as you begin to internalize these seven promises, you are going to become distinctly uncomfortable (remember, I warned you about this a few pages ago). Why? Because you're going to catch yourself routinely breaking them. For example, you will have promised yourself to be responsible and to not blame others for your problems or predicaments, yet you'll catch yourself complaining and pointing fingers. And that is painful. You will have what psychologists call cognitive dissonance, which is trying to simultaneously believe two things that are mutually exclusive. Like believing that you are a responsible and accountable adult but hearing yourself whine and blame others for your problems.

At this point, one of two things *must* happen. Either you stop making the promises to yourself—not because it takes too much time (who doesn't have one minute a day?), but because it's too painful to be a chronic self-liar. Or you keep making the promises, and begin changing your attitudes, your behaviors, and your habits so that you can start doing a better job of keeping them. As you do this, you will begin to see changes in the results you are getting in your work and your life. For example, as you become more responsible and accountable in the way you manage money, you will have more money in the bank. Now you're over the hump. Now, instead of being painful, it's pleasurable to make these promises. Because you know that keeping them is helping you achieve your goals and become the person you were born to be.

THE SELF EMPOWERMENT
PLEDGE

Seven Simple Promises That Will Change Your Life

Monday's Promise: Responsibility
I will take complete responsibilty for my health, my happiness, my success, and my life, and will not blame others for my problems or predicaments.

Tuesday's Promise: Accountability
I will not allow low self-esteem, self-limiting beliefs, or the negativity of others to prevent me from achieving my authentic goals and from becoming the person I am meant to be.

Wednesday's Promise: Determination
I will do the things I'm afraid to do, but which I know should be done. Sometimes this will mean asking for help to do that which I cannot do by myself.

Thursday's Promise: Contribution
I will earn the help I need in advance by helping other people now, and repay the help I receive by serving others later.

Friday's Promise: Resilience
I will face rejection and failure with courage, awareness, and perseverance, making these experiences the platform for future acceptance and success.

Saturday's Promise: Perspective
I will have faith that, though I might not understand why adversity happens, by my conscious choice I can find strength, compassion, and grace through my trials.

Sunday's Promise: Faith
My faith and my gratitude for all that I have been blessed with will shine through in my attitudes and in my actions.

www.Pledge-Power.com

Let's get started

Are you ready to get serious about living your values? The journey begins with Authenticity—knowing yourself and being true to the person you are meant to be. It culminates with leadership, because anyone who internalizes and operationalizes *The Twelve Core Action Values* will become the type of person that others look up to and wish to work with and be with—in other words, a leader. In between, you'll pick up valuable ideas and strategies to change your life for the better, and the inspiration to put them to work. So let's get started.

Part 1

Laying a Solid Foundation:
Core Action Values 1 - 6

Core Action Value #1: Authenticity

Core Action Value #2: Integrity

Core Action Value #3: Awareness

Core Action Value #4: Courage

Core Action Value #5: Perseverance

Core Action Value #6: Faith

"A new discipline immediately alters your life direction. You don't change destinations immediately—that is yet to come—but you can change direction immediately, and direction is very important."

JIM ROHN: *Leading an Inspired Life*

The first six Core Action Values will help you lay a solid foundation of character strength. Character is substantially defined by Authenticity and Integrity; it is refined through Awareness, Courage, and Perseverance; and it is reflected in Faith. Character is destiny, and the work that you put into laying this solid foundation will help to assure that your path in life leads to a bright destiny.

Core Action Value #1 is Authenticity

The greatest triumph of the human spirit is to become the unique and special person you were meant to be; the greatest tragedy is to successfully pretend to be someone else.

Authenticity is Core Action Value #1 because it lays a solid foundation for all that follows. One of the greatest triumphs of the human spirit is to become the authentic, meant-to-be "you." And one of the greatest tragedies is to live your life as a fake, pretending to be somebody you're not because you think you'll make more money or impress others (and trust me—you'll worry a lot less what other people think of you if you'll acknowledge how infrequently they think of you!). Here's another reason we begin with Authenticity: If you really take to heart the principles and the action strategies we're going to cover in Core Action Values 2-12, you will be a lot more successful. And I don't want to help you be more successful at becoming a fake!

Cornerstone #1: Self-Awareness

Use internal observation and external feedback to uncover your truest strengths and passions and the "meant to be" you.

Cornerstone #2: Self-Mastery

Stay out of the *Iron Triangle of False Personality*—manage your emotions, keep your ego out of the way, and pursue only authentic ambitions.

Cornerstone #3: Self-Belief

Work to strengthen each level of the *Pyramid of Self-Belief:* Self-Concept, Self-Image, Self-Awareness, and Self-Confidence.

Cornerstone #4: Self-Truth

Use *Direction Deflection Questions*™ to guide your attitudes and your actions, and to come closer to your best self in every dimension of your life.

Module #1
Core Action Value #1 is Authenticity

"To be yourself in a world that is constantly trying to make you something else is the greatest accomplishment."

RALPH WALDO EMERSON

Our goal for this module

Michelangelo said that he did not carve statues, but rather he found big rocks and liberated the forms that were already hidden within them. Our goal for this module is to begin the process of helping you identify the authentic, meant-to-be "you" and then fulfill the potential of that unique individual.

The Zen master was asked how one carves a statue of an elephant. *"It's easy,"* he replied. *"You just find a big rock, then carve away everything that does not look like an elephant."*

Authenticity is a process, not an outcome

Achieving authenticity is a lifelong process in which questions are usually more important than answers; in fact, anybody searching for the one right "answer" will probably be disappointed. Authenticity is a process of personal growth and periodic self-reinvention. It requires work and discipline, getting out of your comfort zone, and humility coupled with self-belief. Authenticity is not a state of being nearly so much as it is a state of becoming, of striving toward the genuine human being that you are truly meant to be. One of the most stressful conditions is acting out of authenticity, pretending to be somebody you're not, or giving in to impulses that reflect poorly on the real you. It is in those situations you are most likely to regret something you have done or said, or to exclaim that you just weren't being yourself. Authenticity does not mean always doing your own thing, letting it all hang out. There are societal norms in our communities and cultural norms within our organizations that must be honored. Likewise, being part of a team often means putting your ego on the back burner.

You were born to be Authentic

I love the phrase "meant to be." To be it connotes something special, something sacred. Like when two strangers meet on a plane and end up becoming best of friends, it has a feel of divine intentionality to it. At a personal level, "meant to be" means being your ideal best self. We each are born with a personal destiny, with an internal blueprint for the person we are meant-to-be. Along the road, there are many temptations to run away from that destiny; it's often frightening to pursue it. But if you stay on the path, or return to the path any time you find that you've strayed, you will achieve the greatest triumph of the human spirit—that of becoming the authentic, meant-to-be "you."

You become authentic by building upon your strengths and passions, not by trying to fix your weaknesses

Most of us have a million (or more) weaknesses, but only one or two amazing God-given strengths. Tragically, the Gallup organization reports that fewer than one-in-five American workers ever uses their greatest strength in their work. One of the best ways for you to become more authentic is to make the time to cultivate those strengths. What do you consider to be your greatest strengths? What sorts of things get you truly excited and passionate? And how can you build more of those things into your life and work?

The three paradoxes of authenticity

It's been said that all great truth is in the form of paradox. A paradox is a statement that appears to contain an internal contradiction, but which actually reflects a higher truth. For example, when the Taoist philosopher Chuang Tzu said that the only way to achieve real happiness is to stop doing things that are calculated to make you happy, he was stating a paradox. You have to think about it for a moment, then you get it: The happiest people aren't happy because they're always having fun; they're happy because they're doing work that matters, and this gives purpose and meaning to their lives.

The First Paradox of Authenticity

You are more likely to be successful by striving to be authentic than you are by striving to be successful.

The Second Paradox of Authenticity

If you truly want to be authentic, you must push yourself past the boundaries of your comfort zone, and at first this will make you feel inauthentic.

The Third Paradox of Authenticity

Being authentic simultaneously liberates you from the need to impress others and enslaves you to the discipline and hard work of becoming your best self.

 ## Rules for the Journey

1) Take the basket off your inner candle and let it shine for the world.

2) Build upon the foundation of your strengths rather than spending all your time and energy trying to compensate for your weaknesses.

3) Do not compare yourself against others—more often than not, you are unfairly comparing you at your worst against them at their best, comparing your weaknesses against their strengths.

4) Don't worry about what other people think of you, but rather be concerned about whether in your own eyes you are acting as your best self.

5) Never pretend to be someone other than the real you because you think you will make more money or gain more status by being a fraud than you would by being genuine.

6) Pay attention to the inner dialog between your best self and your lesser self (aka soul vs. ego); ego is the loud and self-indulgent voice, soul is the quiet and self-sacrificing voice. You will often regret following the voice of ego and rarely regret following the voice of soul.

Take-home exercise: Write in a journal

Begin the practice of regular journal-writing. As Stephen Covey and colleagues point out in their book *First Things First*, journaling is a high-leverage (important but not urgent) activity for self-discovery, goal-setting, and personal reflection. Especially at first, it really doesn't matter what you write, because whatever you do write will tell you something about where you happen to be in your life at that time. Beginning the habit now will pay off for you as we progress through the next 59 modules of this course.

Questions to jump-start your thinking

- Do you view the world as a safe place full of potential friends and opportunities, or as a hostile place full of potential enemies and dangers? How realistic is your view, does it empower or disempower you, and what can you do to change it?

- Describe any activity that you truly enjoy doing. Would you quit your job and do this full-time if you could make half as much money as you do now? Why or why not?

- Your "soul," however you understand the term, steps out of your body and takes on physical shape. Describe what you see and the conversation that takes place.

- Write about a time that some person really hurt your feelings—how you felt and what the lasting effects were. What would you say to that person right now?

- What would you do if every job paid the same and had the same status?

- If you did that work for a year, would your answer still be the same (a good clue that it was an authentic answer)".

- Write about the most surprising thing that has happened to you in the past year. Why would you not have predicted it one year ago?

- What are some things you could do to have more and better friends?

◘ What kind of person do you want to be remembered as having been?

◘ What is the most important legacy you wish to leave?

◘ Imagine that over the next year everything works out far better than you ever thought would be possible—every problem is resolved, every fear is erased, and every doubt is overcome. From that vantage point, think back on today and write about your problems, fears, and anxieties.

◘ What are you willing to give up in order to have the time, energy, and other resources to pursue your greatest dreams?

 ## Extra credit reading

"We come into this world with a specific, personal destiny. We have a job to do, a calling to enact, a self to become. We are who we are from the cradle, and we're stuck with it. Our job in this lifetime is not to shape ourselves into some ideal we imagine we ought to be, but to find out who we already are and become it."

STEVEN PRESSFIELD: *The War of Art: Break through the Blocks and Win Your Inner Creative Battles*

Something to think about

Who would you be if you didn't have to try and be all the things you think other people think you ought to be?

Module #2
The First Cornerstone of Authenticity is Self-Awareness

"We shall not cease from exploration and the end of all our exploring will be to arrive where we started and know the place for the first time."

T.S. ELIOT

Our goal for this module

Socrates said that the greatest of wisdom was to know yourself. This is easier said than done! Our goal for this module is to begin the process by identifying who you are not (but might think you are), and asking questions that can help you get to the root of your authentic, meant-to-be best self.

Think about this paradox. There are six billion (give or take a few hundred million) souls on the face of the Earth. Of all those billions of faces, the only one that you will never be able to see is the one that is most important to you—your own. You can glimpse approximations—a photograph, a reflection in the mirror, a cameo shadow, a friend's description—but you are forever barred from directly laying eyes upon your own face. That's a great metaphor for self-awareness. It requires indirect measures. The more willing you are to make the journey of inner exploration, the more certain it is that you will discover and become the meant-to-be you.

You are a moving target

The greatest form of wisdom is to know yourself. Socrates said that, and he is believed to have been one of the wisest of the wise. That's easier said than done, isn't it? For one thing, you are a moving target. The "you" of today is a different person than the "you" of ten years ago (perhaps a very different person than the you of ten minutes ago!). So which one is the real you? All of them? None of them? The question is impossible to answer. What is important is that you keep asking it.

It might be difficult, painful, and frightening, this process of seeing who you are, of learning who you are meant to be. But it can also launch you onto a journey through which you find a higher sense of meaning and purpose in the work you do, and a greater sense of joy and adventure in the life you lead. And I emphasize the word "journey," because self-awareness is not something that you finish, like learning the alphabet. Rather, it's like learning a new language. No matter how much you learn, there are always deeper levels of understanding to be gained by reading and conversing. And every bit of new knowledge leads in turn to more questions.

Knowing who you are begins with knowing who you are not

The universal icebreaker question is, of course, *"What do you do?"* On the basis of how you answer that question, people will assume that they know who you are, and put you in a little box—a box that says "big-shot executive" or "just a housewife" or some other superficial categorization. Of course, these superficial stereotypes are not "you," but it's easy to become overly identified with your various attributes and make the mistake of thinking that they are the real you. Knowing who you are begins with knowing who you are not. You are not:

- ◻ ... the roles you play.

- ◻ ... your thoughts, moods, and emotions.

- ◻ ... what other people think of you.

- ◻ ... your past or your future.

- ◻ ... your Myers Briggs score.

In what other ways might you confuse your attributes with being you?

You are not your:

√ moods and emotions
| thoughts and wishes
| body
⚷ Myers Briggs test results
🕐 activities
δ anger and hatred
α hobbies and interests
Y alma mater, GPA, degrees, IQ
φ ethnic heritage, race, color, creed
✝ religious beliefs
☐ handicaps and limitations
| fears, worries, and anxieties
☠ addictions
∪ possessions
♣ zodiac sign
≈ eating habits
ε job, occupation, or business card
⊙ feelings for others
◎ reaction to others' feelings about you
↗ past successes
↘ past failures
☺ relationships

You can rewire your brain by changing your thinking

One of the most exciting fields of brain research today is an area called neuroplasticity. Until very recently, it was believed that the human brain was fixed at some point in late adolescence, and thereafter no longer capable of physical change. One implication of this belief was the assumption that people are hardwired with a certain level of programmed helplessness. Recent research has shown, however, that the brain can actually rewire itself at any age. For example, when adults learns to play a string instrument, the part of the brain that controls the left hand, the fingers of which move rapidly across the strings, develops much more than the part that controls the right hand, which simply strums or holds a bow. But here's something that's even more exciting—something that should absolutely knock your socks off; the same growth occurs when somebody simply visualizes playing the violin without actually doing it!

This finding has profound implications for your own self-talk, self-image, and self-belief, and thus for your subsequent success in life. It means that simply visualizing yourself doing the things that you need to do in order to be successful can begin the process of rewiring your brain to facilitate those actions. Let's say, for example, that you're terrified of public speaking. Repeatedly visualizing yourself giving a great talk can actually rewire your brain by creating synaptic connections for enhanced memory, emotional control, and the other factors that go into delivering a great speech. In other words, there is a scientific basis to the old dictum, *"fake it 'til you make it."*

> **"[W]e are seeing evidence of the brain's ability to remake itself throughout adult life, not only in response to outside stimuli, but even in response to directed mental effort. We are seeing, in short, the brain's potential to correct its own flaws and enhance its own capabilities."**

> JEFFREY SCHWARTZ (WITH SHARON BEGLEY): *The Mind and the Brain: Neuroplasticity and the Power of Mental Force*

 Rules for the Journey

1) Keep writing in your journal, and periodically go back and review what you've been saying to yourself.

2) Pay careful attention to the inner dialog that goes on in your head, and recognize that virtually all negative and disempowering self-talk is not really your own voice, but rather the echoes of hurtful and inhibiting things that others said to you in the distant past.

3) In setting your course for the journey of life, the questions you ask are far more important than the answers you receive.

4) Be constantly aware that the core mission of Madison Avenue advertisers, movie and television producers, news broadcasters, and the rest of the media is to convince you that being you is not sufficient. The more you buy into this falsehood, the less likely it is that you will discover and become the meant-to-be you.

5) When people ask you the universal icebreaker question, see how long you can put off telling them what you do for a living and instead tell them about some of the things that make you who you really are.

Take-home exercise: 360 yourself

Marshall Goldsmith (author of *What Got You Here Won't Get You There*) is a prominent executive coach. He says that one of the first things he does in any coaching assignment is a 360-degree assessment of his new client. Why? Because we can never be completely objective about ourselves—the external feedback helps us have a more realistic self-awareness. You can adapt this practice to your own quest for authenticity. Do a 360-degree evaluation of yourself by asking family members, friends, and co-workers to share their impressions with you. Give them a questionnaire form and stamped envelope addressed to you, and ask them to anonymously answer questions like these:

- What do you think are my greatest strengths?
- When do you see me at my happiest, and what am I doing at those times?
- What is the most important change I need to make in myself?
- What do you think would be my ideal job?
- What is the most important contribution you think I can make?

 ## Extra credit reading

"Healing may not be so much about getting better, as about letting go of everything that isn't you—all of the expectations, all of the beliefs—and becoming who you are."

RACHEL NAOMI REMEN: *Kitchen Table Wisdom: Stories that Heal*

Something to think about

Do you want to be one <u>of</u> a million or one <u>in</u> a million?

Module #3
The Second Cornerstone of Authenticity is Self-Mastery

"I count him braver who overcomes his desires than him who overcomes his enemies; for the hardest victory is the victory over self."

ARISTOTLE

Our goal for this module

To recognize **The Iron Triangle of False Personality** and how it can cause us to be our own worst enemies, and to commit to doing a better job of managing ego, emotions, and ambition to prevent this from happening.

Do you remember the scene from the *Star Wars* movie where Luke Skywalker confronts his worst enemy in a dark tunnel but, upon striking out with his light saber, discovers that he's been looking in a mirror? More than we care to admit, Luke's story is our story: we are the enemy in the tunnel; unless we are able to smash that enemy, we remain mired in the tunnel and cannot escape to the bright world outside.

Meet your own worst enemy

Being absolutely honest with yourself, answer these questions:

> *Have you ever said or done something that you later regretted?*
>
> *Found yourself putting off doing something important?*
>
> *Failed to take action for fear of rejection or fear of failure?*

If you answered yes to any (or all) of these three questions, then bring your two hands together and shake hands with your own worst enemy. Several years ago, I read a book entitled *How Come Every Time I Get Stabbed in the Back My Fingerprints Are All Over the Knife?* (by Jerry Harvey). That's what happens when you fail the test of self-mastery—you end up acting as your own worst enemy, stabbing yourself in the back.

Self-mastery is more important than education, experience, technical qualifications, or who you know when it comes to your long-term career success. Self-mastery underlies the ability to manage impulsiveness and channel energy into productive directions; to build lasting and rewarding relationships with other people; and to build the foundation for a fruitful professional career and a satisfying personal life. Your future success at achieving your goals, overcoming the inevitable troubles of life, and withstanding temptation is being determined *right now* by the work you do on self-mastery and character development. In this module, we'll get to know "your own worst enemy" a little better, and work on strategies to make sure that he/she doesn't derail your plans and dreams.

Escape the Iron Triangle of False Personality

Self-mastery requires escaping the confines of the *Iron Triangle of False Personality*. The points of this triangle are Ego, Emotion, and Ambition. A healthy ego, positive emotions, and authentic ambitions are good things. Problems are guaranteed, however, when ego, emotions, and ambition are calling the shots instead of being effectively managed.

Ego strength is important for not allowing your own self-imposed limitations or the negativity of others to hold you back; unfortunately, an out-of-control ego can distort your perception of yourself and others, lead to short-term what's-in-it-for-me thinking, and cause self-sabotaging attitudes and behaviors.

Emotions make us uniquely and beautifully human, but they are also notoriously fickle and often inappropriately negative; reacting to emotions can cause self-destructive behaviors, resulting in you saying or doing things that you later regret.

Ambition is a valuable source of motivation and drive when it is authentic, but inauthentic ambitions (often pursued in order to satisfy ego and emotion) can create profound unhappiness and a sense of failure in life. Human beings are naturally ambitious—otherwise we would all still be hunting and gathering in the forests. Unfortunately, in our materialistic and image-conscious society it's easy to be driven by ambitions that are dictated by ego rather than those which please the soul. Sometimes, simply asking the question, *"Why do I want this?"* can help you ferret out whether an ambition is ego-driven or soul-directed.

The Iron Triangle Of False Personality

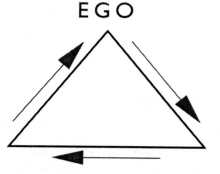

EGO

3. Because they are painful, we respond to those emotions by generating ambitions to make them go away. Unfortunately, those ambitions—precisely because they are in response to emotional heat—are often counterproductive.

1. Ego is injured by a painful occurrence such as being fired from a job, so it...

2. Stirs up a hornet's nest of painful emotions like fear, anger, vengefulness, envy, and resentment.

AMBITION   **EMOTION**

When you're trapped inside *The Iron Triangle of False Personality* you often see a distorted caricature of both yourself—typically weaker and more flawed than is actually the case—and of the world around you—typically more hostile and threatening than it really is. *"Who are you?"* is ultimately a spiritual question, because when you break out of *The Iron Triangle of False Personality*, what you find on the other side is your soul—the ideal, meant-to-be you.

 ## Rules for the Journey

1) Clean up your language; profanity and trash-talk are the vernacular of your lesser self, and when you talk that way, you are letting the rest of the world know that your lesser self is currently running your show.

2) Be conscious in selecting your reference group, which is the fancy name that sociologists give to the people you choose to spend time with. Over time, you will be ineluctably influenced by their beliefs, attitudes, and behaviors, so choose wisely.

3) Absolutely refuse to be party to rumor-mongering; as soon as the gossiping starts, either stop the conversation or walk away from it.

4) Be careful to distinguish between gut feel and intuition. Gut feel is an emotional reaction that says more about you than whatever it is you are reacting to, and will often cause you to act in ways that are counterproductive and self-sabotaging. Intuition, on the other hand, is the apparently-sudden coalescing of observations collected over time into a conclusion or decision; intuition will rarely serve you wrong.

5) Visualize negative self-talk for what it really is: mental graffiti. Create a mental image of a janitor who lives up there in the attic of your mind (*The Janitor in Your Attic*™), then visualize your janitor making rounds to erase the graffiti of negative self-talk and take down the distorted reflections of poor self-image, and replace them with words and images that are positive and supportive of your ideal self and your authentic dreams.

6) Commit yourself to always being an energy faucet who lifts up the people around you with a spark of your energy, and to never be an energy drain who drags people down by sucking the life out of them with your own negativity and pessimism.

 ## Take-home exercise: Put your lesser self in a box

For the next week, put your lesser self into a mental box and keep him or her locked up. That means that for one week, you will not whine or complain about anything; you will not use foul or profane language; you will not play the role of victim or martyr; you will not engage in gossip—not even passively listen to other people gossip; and you will confront the inner voice of negative self-talk and replace it with affirmations that are positive and empowering (and, frankly, more likely to be true than the lies of the voice of negativity).

Extra credit reading

"To the degree that our emotions get in the way of or enhance our ability to think and plan, to pursue training for a different goal, to solve problems and the like, they define the limits of our capacity to use our innate mental abilities, and so determine how we do in life. And to the degree to which we are motivated by feelings of enthusiasm and pleasure in what we do— even by an optimal degree of anxiety—they propel us to accomplishment. It is in this sense that emotional intelligence is a master aptitude, a capacity that profoundly affects all other abilities, either facilitating or interfering with them."

DANIEL GOLEMAN: *Emotional Intelligence*

Something to think about

Imagine yourself wearing a wrist bracelet that said "WWTRMD?"—*"What Would The Real Me Do?"* How would that change your attitudes and behaviors? Would you be pursuing dreams and goals that you are now putting off?

Module #4
The Third Cornerstone of Authenticity is Self-Belief

"All things are possible for one who believes."

MARK 9:23

Our goal for this module

To create a solid foundation for future progress and success by building upon the four levels of *The Pyramid of Self-Belief.*

When Admiral DuPont reported to admiral Farragut the failure of Union ships under his command to break into the Confederate-held Charleston Harbor during the Civil War, he recounted all of his excuses. After he had finished, Farragut said, *"DuPont, there was one reason more."* And what, DuPont asked, might that be? Farragut replied, *"You did not break into the harbor because you did not believe you could do it."* The following year, Farragut himself demonstrated the power of belief. He had himself tied to the mast of his flagship as he led the Union fleet into Mobile Harbor. When one of his ships was sunk by a Confederate mine, Farragut hollered, *"Damn the torpedoes, full speed ahead."* Mobile was taken that day.

Build upon The Pyramid of Self-Belief

Self belief is developed at four levels. Imagine a 4-step pyramid, with self-concept at the foundation, self-image and self-esteem in between, and self confidence at the top. Each element rests upon those below, and the whole process is iterative. In other words, working on changing any element of the pyramid will cascade through the whole.

Level One, Self-Concept

An underlying awareness, either implicit or explicit, of your role as a human being in this universe. What do you see when you look around you: a world of scarcity and risk, or a world of abundance and opportunity? What is your concept of a higher power, and of your relationship to that higher power? Questions like these cannot be answered in an absolute sense, but rather depend largely on what you choose to see as you look around you and within you.

Level Two, Self-Image

What do you see when you look in the mirror? A winner? A victim? You will never on a sustained basis exceed your self image. If your self image is that of being a victim, no matter what happens, you will always be a victim. On the other hand, the self-perceived winner who loses everything will eventually find a way to get it all back, and probably sooner rather than later.

Level Three, Self-Esteem

Do you like what you see when you look in the mirror? People with high self-esteem get a lot done and make substantial contributions; people with low self-esteem tend not to. Self-esteem is not arrogance (quite to the contrary), rather it is holding yourself to high expectations because you appreciate your gifts and want to share them with others.

Level Four, Self-Confidence

Do you believe that you have skills and resources to meet the challenges of your life and to effectively pursue your dreams and goals? Genuine self-confidence is usually quiet, as opposed to the loud boastfulness of arrogance. You are not born with self-confidence, it is earned through experience.

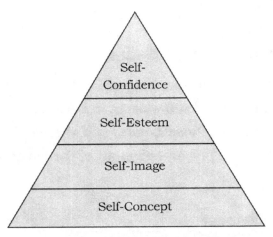

The Pyramid of Self-Belief

Self-belief is hardest to find when you need it most

It is easy to believe in yourself when everything is going great, Lady Luck is in your court, you've got money in the bank, and everyone loves you and believes in you. It's when you've fallen on your face, the till is empty, and you feel like you've been abandoned that you most need to believe in yourself and in your dreams. That is, of course, when it is hardest to do. It is also very often precisely at these most difficult times that the greatest leverage exists to bring about a dramatic change in your situation. If you can maintain your self-belief during times of adversity, you frequently emerge stronger, more focused and more determined than ever. The secret is to prepare yourself ahead of time, before adversity strikes, to maintain your motivation and your self-belief, because if you wait until bad things happen, it will be a whole lot more difficult.

A tough love message

Low self-esteem (buying into those negative labels) is more often than not just an excuse for laziness and cowardice. If you really believe that the members of a group don't like you, and suspect that it's because you don't deserve to be liked, you won't make much of an effort to become part of the group. If you really believe that you're not capable of making something happen, you probably won't find the courage to try. In either case, you end up creating a self-fulfilling prophecy. That's why I believe that we all have an absolute obligation to challenge self-limiting labels and enhance our own self-image and self-esteem—so that we will have the courage and the energy to make a difference.

 ## Rules for the Journey

1) Stay out of the victim spiral where Learned Helplessness descends into Blame Game which deteriorates into Victim Syndrome.

2) Be tough *with* yourself, not tough *on* yourself.

3) Self-belief is not arrogance. People who need to put down others in order to puff up themselves are not reflecting high self-esteem, but rather trying to cover up their own insecurity. Even worse, arrogance often underlies hubris—the pride that comes before the fall—because arrogant people are not

particularly objective about what's really going on around them, open to legitimate criticism, or willing to make needed changes in their approach to life and to other people.

4) Dare to never compare.

5) Avoid negative people, and go out of your way to seek out positive people.

6) Whether consciously or not, in order to understand ourselves and the world around us, we rely heavily upon metaphors. To say, *"I'm a pussycat"* conveys a whole range of meanings. Change the metaphor to, *"I'm a bulldog"* and you get a whole new range of meanings. With self-awareness, you can become more cognizant of the metaphors that you subconsciously use to define and describe yourself; changing those metaphors can be a powerful way of building self-belief. Think of some of the metaphors that you use (consciously or subconsciously) to describe yourself and your place in the world.

7) Without action, positive thinking and positive self-talk are little more than good intentions. So whatever empowering questions you ask of yourself, whatever positive affirmations you write for yourself—take action. Just do it, and do it now.

 Take-home exercise: Make your own motivational tape or CD

Would you like to see the world's greatest motivational speaker? Right this minute? If so, go stand in front of a mirror. He or she will be right there, looking back at you. That's because nobody can motivate you but you, and the things that you say to yourself will either motivate you or they will de-motivate you. *Try this:* Over the next 30 days, start making notes about the things you like about yourself, about your future goals and dreams, and about the things you know you must do in order to become your ideal best self and to achieve those goals and dreams. Then, on a day when you are emotionally flying high, sit down (better yet, stand up) at a microphone and record your own motivational audiotape or CD. Program yourself with *you* telling *you* how great *you* are—especially on the days that you are having a hard time believing it.

Extra credit reading

"Believe me when I tell you that if you don't step up and fight for you, no one else will. At the same time, I think you may find that the person you most need to stand up to in this world is you... [I]n this war we call life, most of the decisive battles are fought within you."

PHILLIP C. MCGRAW: *Life Strategies: Doing What Works, Doing What Matters*

Something to think about

You are where you are today because of choices you made in the past; you will be where you are in the future as a result of choices you make starting now. So don't blame anyone else for your problems or predicaments.

Module #5
The Fourth Cornerstone of Authenticity is Self-Truth

➔ ➔

"This above all: to thine own self be true, and it must follow, as the night the day, thou cans't not then be false to any man."

WILLIAM SHAKESPEARE

Our goal for this module

To make a commitment of being true to our best selves, and to utilize *Direction Deflection Questions* to steer us toward the attitudes and behaviors that are consistent with being that meant-to-be best self.

You arrive for your flight a bit early. There are six other people already there in the waiting area. Three of them are really weird. Which three? One man is over by the window doing push-ups. The man seated nearby is drinking a super-sized latte and munching on a humongous cinnamon roll. Which one is weird? Over in one corner a young father is engaged in a boisterous wrestling match with his little boy. In the other corner, another young father is scolding his little boy, telling him that if he doesn't sit still and be quiet, he'll lose TV privileges for a week. Which one is weird? A woman is talking on her cell phone. You overhear her complaining that they'd forced her to fly from Topeka to Chicago on one of those tiny regional jets with the uncomfortable seats, and now her flight to San Diego was delayed by four hours, ruining the start of her vacation. Not only that, the closest Starbucks is in the next terminal and she's too tired to walk. Nearby, another woman is kneeling in front of her seat with her hands folded. You overhear her thanking God for her safe arrival in Chicago and praying for the safety of her son who is serving overseas in the military. Which one is weird?

Authenticity does not mean...

Authenticity does not necessarily mean nonconformance, doing your own thing, or letting it all hang out. There are societal norms in our communities and cultural norms within our organizations that must be honored. Likewise, being part of a team often means putting your ego on the back burner. To be authentic means learning how to be genuine within the larger context of the organizations and society of which you are a part.

Meant-to-be does not mean preordained. Becoming the authentic, meant-to-be "You" will require conscious making of hard choices, and a commitment to disciplined action. Meant-to-be does not mean that something will happen spontaneously; it means that you are meant to make it happen. It's up to you whether or not you will make it happen.

Success won't do it (nor will failure)

To a greater or lesser degree, most of us are waiting for some outside event to move us in the desired direction—completing the degree, getting the promotion, or (heaven forbid!) winning the lottery. For better or worse, however, success will not make you more authentic, success will not empower you, it will only make you more of who you already are. Ditto failure. Winning a truckload of unearned money will make the self-perceived victim feel like even more of a victim within short order. Failing in a business venture will simply steel the self-perceived winner's determination to prevail the next time around.

Authenticity is the first step on a journey that culminates in leadership

It takes discernment and wisdom to distinguish between authentic dreams and delusions of grandeur, but a true leader must be able to make that distinction. Authenticity is the first of *The Twelve Core Action Values* for the very good reason that it is the foundation upon which all else is built. As leadership expert Warren Bennis writes in his book *On Becoming a Leader*, leadership is first a matter of being, then doing. Bennis writes: *"Becoming a leader is synonymous with becoming yourself. It is precisely that simple, and it is also that difficult."* The best leaders don't aspire to leadership for its own sake, but rather because they must lead others in order to achieve some higher end.

Rules for the Journey

1) Accept yourself as you are, warts and all, and don't insult yourself by comparing you at your worst with other people at their best.

2) Work for continuous self-improvement—work on removing the warts, especially those that reflect character issues you're not proud of.

3) Take complete and absolute responsibility for your circumstances and your outcomes. You are where you are today because of choices you have made in the past, and you will be where you are tomorrow as a result of choices you make in the future.

4) Become a more effective time manager. People with low self-esteem are notoriously poor time managers, especially to the extent they waste their time (and their lives) in front of the boob tube. One of the most immediate ways you can begin raising your self-esteem is by putting your time to more effective use.

5) Avoid negative people, and go out of your way to seek out positive people. Over time, you take on the attitudes of the people you spend your time with; make sure that you're investing in yourself by spending time with people who are positive and optimistic.

6) Believe in other people. Be what I call a Dionarap—which is the word paranoid spelled backwards. It's easier to believe in yourself when you also believe in other people.

7) Decide who you want to be and start acting the part until it feels natural, then graduate to a bigger part and start rehearsing.

8) Appreciate this paradox of self-truth: To be true to yourself, you must be true to something that is bigger than your self.

Take-home exercise: Use DDQs, the questions that will change your life

The Direction Deflection Question (DDQ) is a powerful tool for helping you be true to yourself, your ideals, and your dreams. Here's how it works: You're heading in a certain direction, and you stop and ask yourself whether that's really where you want to go. If it's not where you want to go, then you ask yourself where you *do* want to go, and what you could (should) be doing *right now* to move you in that direction. This is the quintessential DDS: *Will what I'm about to do or say help me be my ideal best self?*

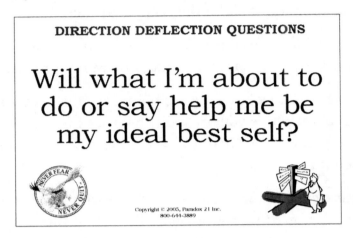

You will note that the DDQ really comprises three questions. First, you cannot begin to even ask whether something will help you be your best self (as a parent, as a professional, as a time and money manager, or in any other capacity) if you haven't first put some thought into who that best self is. Second, you ask yourself if what you are about to do or say will help you come closer to that ideal role (hint: if you don't hear the answer "no" quite a bit, then you probably aren't being very honest with yourself). Third, if the answer to the second question is "no," then you ask yourself what you *would* be doing if you were being your best self (hint: if it's more difficult and challenging than what you were about to do, it's probably the right answer).

The DDQ is infinitely adaptable. I've helped people write DDQs that in turn helped them more effectively control fear, anger, and other negative emotions; that helped them lose weight or manage their money more effectively; and that helped them do a better job of pursuing their big dreams. Here are just a few examples of DDQs that could help you:

Will what I'm about to spend my hard-earned money on help me achieve my goals of being debt-free and financially independent? If I were being my ideal self, would I make this expenditure?

Is what I'm about to put into my mouth going to contribute to my health and fitness goals? Will I starve to death if I don't eat this and go for a walk instead?

Does what I'm about to say to my child reflect the parent that I want to be? What would I do if I were being the parent I know I want to be?

Is what I'm about to spend my precious time doing going to help me achieve one of my important goals? If not, what is the single most important thing I could be doing with my time right now (and why aren't I doing that instead of what I'm about to be doing)?

You've probably read that it takes 28 days (give or take a few) to establish a new habit. Well, the same can probably be said for internalizing and operationalizing a DDQ. If you can make it stick for one month, chances are that it's going to become a part of your habit pattern and a part of your worldview. In fact, before very long you will look back with astonishment at the time and money you once wasted, at the way you once abused your body, at the way you once treated others. And you'll be proud of the changes you've made.

 ## Extra credit reading

"Are [highly accomplished people] also special and gifted and divine? No more than you are, no more than I am. The only difference, the very only one, is that they have begun to understand what they really are and have begun to practice it."

RICHARD BACH: Jonathan Livingston Seagull

 Something to think about

You'd worry a lot less what other people think of you if you'd acknowledge how infrequently they think of you!

Authenticity is the essential first step down the long road that culminates in leadership. To know who you are and to strive to be the best at being that person, and never pretend to be someone else, is the greatest of challenges and the greatest of triumphs.

Core Action Value #2 is Integrity

Without integrity, short-term winners inevitably become long-term losers. Integrity is the foundation of trust and respect.

Cornerstone #1: Honesty

Be absolutely honest—especially with yourself. Genuine honesty is more than just not telling lies—it is living the truth.

Cornerstone #2: Reliability

Do what you say you're going to do, when you say you're going to do it, and do it to the best of your ability.

Cornerstone #3: Humility

Virtually every failure of integrity begins with arrogance on the part of those responsible; humility is an essential ingredient of effective leadership.

Cornerstone #4: Stewardship

Honor the obligation to be a good steward of your own resources, the resources of your organization, and of the fragile world in which we live.

"I am absolutely convinced that in most cases, prioritizing trust—actively seeking to establish it, grow it, restore it, and wisely extend it—will bring personal and organizational benefits that far exceed any other path"

STEPHEN M.R. COVEY: *The Speed of Trust: The One Thing that Changes Everything*

Module #6
Core Action Value #2 is Integrity

"Character isn't inherited. One builds it daily by the way one thinks and acts, thought by thought, action by action."

HELEN GAHAGAN DOUGLAS

Our goal for this module

To understand that integrity is more than just ethics, but rather a commitment to living and acting upon core values in every dimension of your life—personal and professional.

One day the ruler of an ancient kingdom visited the prison. He stopped at many of the cells and spoke with prisoners. Each imprisoned man protested his innocence, except for the last convict with whom the king spoke. This prisoner, alone among all the others, admitted his guilt. At that, the king shouted to the prison guards: *"Throw this scoundrel out of this prison, before he corrupts all the innocents!"*

Character is destiny

As the Greek philosopher Heraclitus said, character is destiny. Cultivating strength of character is an arduous process subject to backsliding without constant vigilance. Integrity is a matter of character, but it is also a matter of competence. It is through integrity that one earns the trust and the respect of others. This comes as a result of being the kind of person they are (character) as well as the things they do and how they do those things (competence).

"Without integrity, even winning ends up losing."

Integrity means wholeness

The root of the word integrity is "integer," and that word implies a united and undivided whole. So to be a person of integrity means to be whole—to be guided by the same values at work and at home. At a higher level, it implies that wholeness of humanity, that we are all children of the same God. To demean or diminish another person because of their occupation, race, religion or any other factor is to violate their dignity and your integrity.

"A man is both a seed and in some degree also a gardener, for good or ill. I am impressed by the degree in which the development of 'character' can be a product of conscious intention, the will to modify innate tendencies in desired directions; in some cases the change can be great and permanent."

J.R.R. TOLKIEN: *The Letters of J.R.R. Tolkien*

Integrity is the value – trust and respect are the outcomes

When people talk about their values, and when organizations create their values statements, they often include the word "trust." But trust is not a value, it is an outcome. You earn people's trust by being a person of integrity. And earning that trust is a lot like climbing a mountain: the trip up can be long and arduous, but with a single misstep, you can make a fast and painful return to the bottom, perhaps never to ascend again.

Like trust, respect is also an outcome, not a value. Would you respect someone you can't trust—someone who lacks integrity? Just as trust is an outcome of acting with integrity, respect is a corollary that comes with earning that trust. Self-respect, and the respect of others, is built upon a foundation of acting with integrity—of gaining self-trust and earning the trust of others. So trust and respect are not values, they are attributes you *earn* by acting with integrity. You will neither trust nor respect someone who lies to you, someone who cannot be relied upon to fulfill their commitments.

 ## Rules for the Journey

1) Avoid people of questionable integrity, people who are not trustworthy, and people who seem to get their greatest joy by putting other people down. Not only do you risk seeming guilty by association, over time it is virtually inevitable that you will absorb some of the attitudes and begin to mimic the behaviors of these people.

2) Do not participate in gossip, not even as a passive listener. Passing rumors and talking about people behind their backs is, without exception, a violation of integrity.

3) Use *Direction Deflection Questions* (DDQs) to guide you along the path with integrity by doing an internal check to prevent you from saying or doing things that you will later regret because these words and actions were not "in integrity" with your best self.

4) Look past superficialities (including what someone does to make a living, the kind of car they happen to drive, and their physical appearance); avoiding such snap judgments protects their dignity and your integrity.

5) Think about the difficult situations you might face in the future—with your job, with your finances, with your family. By anticipating such events, and visualizing how your best self would handle them, you are more likely to allow that best self to take command when they do arise.

 ## Take-home exercise: Catalog your problem areas

Two things that often get people into trouble on the integrity front are being behind in their obligations and being in over their heads in debt. A good exercise is to make a list of areas where you are behind, either with regard to time or money. Which of these issues have the greatest potential to put so much pressure on you that you might feel pushed to act in ways that you later regret? What can you do now (if you are not sure what I mean by that word "now", check your dictionary) to prevent this from happening?

 ## Extra credit reading

"Integrity means being whole, unbroken, undivided. It describes a person who has united the different parts of his or her personality, so there is no longer a split in the soul... For the person of integrity, life may not be easy but it is simple: Figure out what is right and do it. All other considerations come in second."

HAROLD KUSHNER: *Living a Life That Matters*

Something to think about

Integrity begins with introspection; you must learn to trust and respect yourself before you can expect that others will trust and respect you.

Module #7
The First Cornerstone of Integrity is Honesty

"A lie can be halfway round the world before the truth has got its boots on."

JAMES CALLAGHAN

Our goal for this module

To fully appreciate that honesty (beginning with self-honesty) is always the best policy, not just on moral but also on practical grounds, and to adopt a commitment to insulate yourself against pressures and temptations to step onto the slippery slope of dishonesty.

I invited Roger Looyenga, the CEO of Auto-Owners Insurance (a Fortune 500 company that is a long-standing Values Coach Client) to be a speaker at one of our seminars on values-based leadership. He shared his company's ten core values, the first of which is honesty. During a discussion about tolerating failure and learning from mistakes, Roger described a situation in which an executive had made a decision which cost the company 200 million dollars. *"Was he fired?"* asked one of the seminar participants. Roger said no.

The questioner was astonished and asked, *"If someone doesn't get fired for losing millions of dollars, what will they be fired for?"* There was not a moment's hesitation in Roger's reply: *"Being dishonest."* The questioner persisted: *"What if the dishonesty made the company millions of dollars? Would that make a difference?"* Again, there was no hesitation in Roger's reply: *"Absolutely not. For one thing, you cannot make money at Auto-Owners by being dishonest, because as soon as the transgression was discovered, we'd pay it back. Besides, we can recover from financial losses. But once a company has been tarnished with the stain of dishonesty, it's almost impossible to restore its good reputation."*

Honesty begins with yourself

The first cornerstone of integrity is honesty—being honest with yourself, and then with others. In this respect, integrity ties back to Core Action Value #1, Authenticity, since self-awareness is an essential ingredient of self-honesty. If you look into any situation in which a politician, a businessperson, or anyone else has engaged in unethical and harmful behavior, you will almost always find that their behavior began with an act of self-deception, including denial, rationalization, and self-justification. If you are not being honest with yourself, you will eventually be dishonest with others.

When people deceive themselves it can lead to serious, even devastating, consequences. Self-deception by both Hitler and Stalin led to gross errors and ghastly casualties on both sides of the eastern front during World War II. American auto executives during the 1970s chose the path of self-deception when the Japanese automobile industry began importing higher quality, lower cost cars. This seriously damaged the domestic auto industry and cost thousands of jobs. Self-deception on the part of leaders is one of the most serious threats to organizations and communities, indeed to the welfare of entire nations. Paradoxically, just being aware of the potential of self-deception (which we all have in greater degree than we care to admit) can be liberating.

You almost never "can't"

Anytime you hear yourself telling that you "can't" do something, remind yourself that it's probably not true (and that The Beatles were right: *there's nothing you can do that can't be done*). Whatever it is "I can't" do, you probably can do, especially if it's really important to your being true to your authentic best self. More likely, what you really mean is that it would be difficult, it would be inconvenient, or some other excuse. When you admit to yourself that the achievement is, in fact, within your power, you have taken the first step toward its fulfillment: the step of being honest with yourself. As author Richard Bach wrote in his book *Illusions*, "*You are never given a wish without also being given the power to make it true,*" though he goes on to point out that making it true will probably require working at it.

Just because you believe something doesn't make it true

Honesty often requires a good-sized dollop of humility; just because you believe something doesn't make it true. History is full of examples of "true believers" who caused great harm because they were so convinced in their beliefs that they never considered that they might in fact be wrong. Sometimes, the greatest act of self-honesty is to be very clear about the distinction between opinions and facts, between small truths and great truths (see next section). True honesty (as opposed to true believing) mandates that you acknowledge the possibility that you are wrong. This requires being objective (being willing and able to see the world from a different, even opposing, perspective) and it requires being humble (getting your ego, emotions and personal ambitions out of the way of seeing that bigger picture with clearer eyes).

The "Big Truth" paradox

Physicist Neils Bohr said that, *"The opposite of a small truth is a falsehood. The opposite of a great truth is another great truth."* People who believe their beliefs to be the only truth, meaning that the beliefs of other people are false, are often the cause of polarization, hatred, and violence. It's been said that God has a big tent, and that many paths lead to the top of a mountain. Just because yours is a true path doesn't mean that everyone else is on a false path. If you are unable to put yourself in the shoes of people with opposing viewpoints, if you are unable to see the truth in their perspective (as different as it is from yours), chances are that you are dealing in small truths, not great truths.

 ## Rules for the Journey

1) Beware of arrogance, rationalization, self-justification, and all other forms of self-deception; honesty with others begins with honesty with self.

2) Be cautious to distinguish between opinions and facts, and to remain humble and open to the possibility that no matter how fervently you happen to believe something, it does not mean that people who believe differently are necessarily wrong. Likewise, true honesty (as opposed to true believing) mandates that you acknowledge the possibility that you are wrong.

3) Challenge your own self-confining beliefs and self-imposed limitations, which are often reflected in the utterance of the toxic two words *"I can't."*

4) If you catch yourself in the act of self-deception, or of being dishonest with others, take immediate action to return to the truth. Honesty begins by being honest with yourself, and deception of others most often begins with self-deception.

5) Do a reality check on yourself: in what ways are you currently practicing self-deception (if you don't think you are, it's probably a pretty good sign that you are).

Take-home exercise: Analyze, and if necessary change, your reference group

Research has shown that most people have much less inner strength and will-power than they give themselves credit for (for an excellent summary, see Malcolm Gladwell's book *The Tipping Point*). Given this, you will be far more successful in life if you simply stay away from negative influences (including people, places, and media) rather than try to resist being influenced by them. One of the most important choices you will ever make is the people and the groups with which you associate. What sociologists call a reference group, the people or organizations you identify with, can have a profound impact on your values, attitudes, and actions—often much more of an influence than we care to admit. The best way to maintain your integrity is to stay away from people who lack integrity.

Extra credit reading

"Defining your moral standards serves as an ethical compass that prevents you from straying off course when the winds of temptation begin howling around your ship of life. Millions of people continually crash on the rocks of bad consequences, often suffering irreparable damage, because they allowed themselves to get caught in rough waters without first making certain that they had their ethical compasses abroad. It's imperative to understand that for any strategy or plan of action to be sound, it must begin with a solid moral foundation. Without such a foundation, anything a person tries to build is destined to crumble."

ROBERT J. RINGER: *Million Dollar Habits*

Something to think about

When you gain something by telling a lie, you lose something far more important. When you lose something as a result of telling the truth, you gain something far more valuable.

Module #8
The Second Cornerstone of Integrity is Reliability

"To let oneself be bound by a duty from the moment you see it approaching is part of the integrity that alone justifies responsibility."

DAG HAMMARSKJÖLD

Our goal for this module

To appreciate the profound importance of being reliable, beginning with knowing that you can rely on yourself to do what you've said you are going to do, when you said you are going to do it, and do it to the best of your ability.

It's easy to live up to your commitments when times are easy. Integrity demands that you also live up to them when times are tough. Your integrity *will* be tested, that is only a matter of time and you *will* need to be strong in order to meet that test.

Reliability and trust

The road to hell is not paved with good intentions. You *should have* more good intentions than you could ever possibly fulfill. If there is a road to hell, it is more likely to be paved with broken promises, so promise only what you can actually do. As wonderful as good intentions are, remember that they are very difficult to sell until you establish a reputation as someone who converts them into productive action. That is how you earn the trust of people to whom you make promises.

Reliability and Authenticity

How popular do you suppose Coca Cola would be if you never knew what color it was going to be—one day orange and the next day green? If you're old enough to remember the customer rebellion when the folks at Coke tried to tweak the formula (the "New Coke" disaster), you know the answer—people want to know what to expect when they open a can of Coke—or walk into a McDonald's, or go into the operating room for surgery. An important part of being authentic is being reliable, so that others know what to expect of you—so that you know what to expect of yourself.

The more clear that authentic self-image is in your own mind, the more powerfully motivated you will be to reliably live up to its expectations.

There is no free lunch

In the course of my research for the audio CD album *True Wealth: Your Values and Your Money*, I read a great deal about gambling. One of the most insidious dangers of something as seemingly innocent as buying a lottery ticket is that you send your subconscious a message that you cannot rely upon your own efforts to provide for your future needs and wants, that you're not willing to work and wait but rather are praying for fate or the wheel of fortune to intervene with the proverbial free lunch. I suppose it might be related to memories of Santa Claus, the Tooth Fairy, and the Easter Bunny, but we all want to wake up in the morning and find a nice surprise under the tree, or under our pillow. As most lottery winners learn to their dismay, a free lunch usually causes a bad case of indigestion, and the worst of it is the way it corrodes the "winner's" own sense of self-reliance. The one person to whom you most need to be reliable is yourself. And that gets us to...

Being self-reliable begins with turning pro

I have previously commended Steven Pressfield's little book *The War of Art*, which is about much more than art and creativity. It's about overcoming the single-most pernicious barrier to success in virtually any endeavor that requires initiative, effort, and risk, what he calls Resistance. Steve's prescription for overcoming Resistance is to turn pro, which does not necessarily mean becoming part of a profession or even being paid for what you do. He means this in the sense of taking a professional approach toward our work. It is a powerful prescription for being reliable, for cultivating the discipline that is required so that you will always know that you can rely on yourself to show up. Here are some of the key qualities Pressfield describes for being a real pro:

> **Pros show up for work every day, whether they feel good or not, whether it's raining or sunny outside.** The secret to overcoming procrastination is to work yourself into the right mood rather than waiting to be struck by the right mood before you start your work.

> **They stay on the job all day long, giving the work the best that they have to offer.** John Gardner once commented that the real dropout prob-

lem in America isn't in the school system, it's in the workplace—millions of people physically show up for work in the morning, but have mentally checked out before their first coffee break. The Gallup organization has done research showing that a majority of American workers are not really engaged in their work, and a disturbing number are actively disengaged.

Pros are committed for the long haul. They know there will be obstacles and setbacks, but they continue to show up for the job and give their best to the work, through even the most difficult of times.

Pros are self-validating. The pro does not depend upon the praise of others for motivation, nor does she allow criticism (or the absence of praise) to hinder her efforts.

Pros are worried about mastering the craft itself, not the benefits they might gain from the final product. They rely on themselves to put in the hours of study, preparation, and concentration, even knowing that they cannot rely on the rest of the world to reward their efforts.

The pro knows that you can't overcome fear (of rejection, of failure, of ridicule), but rather that you have to do your work in the face of that fear (*"Do the thing you fear and the death of the fear is certain"* said Ralph Waldo Emerson).

You do not need an agent, a contract, or a sign-on bonus to turn pro. It is an act of will. You simply decide that you will be reliable. You will show up for every day, and every day you will give your best to your work. Perhaps the greatest compliment in the world is to be called "a real pro." One of the most important ways you earn that appellation is to be reliable—beginning with self-reliance and extending outward to being reliable in your dealings with other people.

 ## Rules for the Journey

1) Learn how to say no more often so that you can finish on time with the things you're already said yes to; saying *"I'll think about it"* when someone asks you to do something is a way of buying time so that you can decide if you really have the time to keep the commitment.

2) *"Under promise and over deliver"* is often held out as a formula for excellent customer service, and it is a good one. One of the best ways to become more reliable is to make fewer promises, but to complete the ones you have made on (or ahead of) schedule, and do it with extravagant attention to quality.

3) Do the things that you *need* to get done before you do the things that you *want* to get done; if you start to get behind, be quick to ask for help.

4) Two things that often get people into trouble on the integrity front are being behind in their obligations and being over their heads in debt. Make a list of areas where you are behind, either with regard to time or money. Which of these issues have the greatest potential to put so much pressure on you that you might feel pushed to act in ways that you later regret? What can you do *now* to prevent this from happening?

5) Make a list of all the promises you've made, the deadlines you're expected to meet, the debts you owe (excluding major things such as home mortgage and car loans). Now, do not make any more promises, do not commit yourself to any more deadlines, or take on any new debts until each and every one of the obligations you've already made has been satisfied.

6) Think about how making a more personal and sustained commitment to living and working with integrity can change your life. What commitments are you willing to make to reinforce your own integrity? What sacrifices are you willing to make?

 ## Take-home exercise: Create a "reliability identity" statement

"Absolutely, positively." "Die Hard." "Ready when you are." "There when you need us." "The No Problem People." Many successful companies have built reliability into their very identities. Those words are far more than advertising come-ons: they define the very soul of the business, and prescribe performance expectations for the people who work there. Try writing your own reliability identity statement. Are you *"the one to go to when the chips are down?"* How about *"always a smile on the outside no matter what's happening on the inside?"* Or *"earning and saving my way to financial independence?"* Perhaps yours might be, *"you count on*

me to care." Words are verbal power tools, and over time the words that you use to describe yourself have a profound impact on your character, personality, and identity. Choose them wisely.

 Extra credit reading

"The rules are simple: Don't make agreements you don't want to make. Keep all the agreements you make. Tell the rock-bottom truth if you find you are not going to keep an agreement. Cop to it immediately if you fail to keep an agreement."

GAY HENDRICKS AND KATE LUDEMAN:
The Corporate Mystic

Something to think about

Consider that we all have an addiction to time and an addiction to money. When we feel that we are running out of either, we start to get withdrawal symptoms. Realizing that you are not going to make a deadline, or finally getting around to balancing your checkbook and discovering that every check you wrote last week will bounce, both provoke similar physiological reactions: rapid heartbeat, shortness of breath, a momentary confused daze—the DT's of time/money addiction!

Module #9
The Third Cornerstone of Integrity is Humility

"Do you wish to rise? Begin by descending. You plan a tower that will pierce the clouds? Lay first the foundation of humility."

SAINT AUGUSTINE

Our goal for this module

To encourage personal thoughtfulness and introspection for your own sense of humility, and to gain a deeper understanding of the central role that humility plays in effective leadership.

Two bishops were on their knees at the church altar. *"I'm nothing, Lord!"* they each proclaimed. *"Nothing but a worthless sinner."* As this was going on, the janitor happened by. Seeing the bishops, he too fell to his knees at the altar and cried out, *"I'm nothing, Lord, nothing but a worthless sinner."* The first bishop turned to his colleague and with a look of disdain whispered, *"Now look who thinks he's nothing but a worthless sinner."*

Humility and Level 5 Leadership

Jim Collins, author of the business bestsellers *Built to Last* (with Jerry Porras) and *Good to Great,* describes Level 5 Leadership as a blend of extreme personal humility with intense professional will. As counterintuitive as it might seem, he says that the best of leaders are humble human beings. When you think about it, though, that notion jibes with what we know. For example, two of our most beloved presidents were George Washington and Abraham Lincoln. Both of these men were known for their humility—as well as for their fierce determination to achieve their goals.

Contrast these presidents with men who were equally determined, but who were personally arrogant and self-centered. Lyndon Baines Johnson and Richard M. Nixon were both incredibly driven men, but lacked any sense of humility. Both were acutely concerned for their place in history. It is the tragic irony of each man's career that it was his own hubris (the pride that goes before the fall) which assured that he would be remembered not as a great president, but as a flawed human being.

Consultant John Baldoni writes that humility is *"the essence of effective leadership."* He defined humility as *"acceptance of personal limitations—I cannot do it alone—coupled with a sense of resolve to do something about it—I will enlist the help of others."* He outlined four steps for fostering humility in your leadership style:

1) invite feedback by making it safe to give it;
2) encourage dissent;
3) turn failures into lessons instead of trying to cover them up or rationalize them away; and
4) expect humility in others.

Be open to constructive criticism and welcome the bearers of bad news

Humility can keep you out of a lot of trouble. When you are open to constructive criticism, and when you welcome those who bring you bad news or otherwise tell you things that you really would rather not hear, you can take early action to prevent what could become a damaging situation. In the field of leadership theory, "CEO disease" refers to the fact that the higher one goes in an organization, the less likely they are to be given the absolute and un-doctored truth, but instead to be told what people think they want to hear and to not be told what people think will upset them. To the extent CEO's make decisions on the basis of this flawed picture of the world, they can cause great harm to their organizations and the teams of people who work there.

Humility is the antidote to arrogance and complacence

It seems like every athletic coach that has ever paced a sideline has written a book on his or her formula for success. Read them all and you'll see many different prescriptions for organization, motivation, and the other prerequisites of building a winning sports team. But each and every one of these books will say the same thing about success: the most dangerous time in the history of any individual athlete or athletic team is after they have won it all. That is when the twin threats of complacency and arrogance tend to set in. Here again we see the paradox that humility is a key ingredient in the formula for sustained success.

Appreciate the vast mystery of infinite space and time

Collin Fletcher was the first man to hike solo across the Grand Canyon from end to end, and he wrote a book about it entitled *The Man Who Walked Through Time*. Probably the most significant thing Fletcher came to understand in the course of his trek was the paradox that before you can appreciate your true significance as a human being, you must first accept your relative insignificance in the scope of time and space. One way of maintaining your humility is to be in constant awe of the mysteries of life, and of the natural world around you.

 ## Rules for the Journey

1) Keep in mind the paradox of servant leadership: the most successful leaders combine professional competence and confidence with personal humility.

2) Be honest and aware of how the external environment, including people with whom you associate, influences your attitudes and behaviors.

3) Make time for reading, reflection, and prayer, all of which help you take your focus off yourself and shift it onto the people and the world around you.

4) As your income and wealth increase, keep your life frugal and simple as you increase your commitment to charity for others.

5) Laugh loudest when the joke's on you; genuine humility is often reflected in an ability to laugh at yourself.

 ## Take-home exercise: Distinguish between opinions and principles

Opinions are shaped by what you believe about a certain person, situation, problem, or opportunity. To be humble means to be flexible in your opinions. Remember, just because you believe something doesn't make it true. At the Institute for the Future in Palo Alto, California they advise clients to have "strong opinions that are weakly held." Here's what they mean be that: if you don't have strong opinions about something (say an opportunity that you're thinking about pursuing), you're unlikely to generate the passion necessary to bring about change. But you also need to not be too attached to those opinions because it will prevent you from seeing evidence that runs counter to the beliefs upon which those opinions are based. Principles, on the other hand, are immutable guides for how one lives one's life and does one's work (e.g. "Thou shalt not kill"). Principles do not change with every election or news commentary.

And that brings up the distinction between someone with an opinion and someone standing on a principle. Opinions can be changed with new facts and enlightened consideration. Principles are, almost by definition, carved in stone. Someone with an opinion can say: *"I might be wrong, but here's why I think I'm right."* Someone who is standing on a principle can only say: *"You are wrong because I am right."* Two people who have a different opinion about an issue can have a discussion. Two people are standing upon conflicting principles can only fight. And history has shown that, all too often, fighting is exactly what they do. It is important to know the principles, and the values that undergird those principles, that should guide your life. It's also important to be honest with yourself about the distinction between principles and opinions.

Consider the things about which you feel very strongly (e.g. sex, politics and religion). To what extent is your view shaped by principles and to what extent is it shaped by opinions? Being honest with yourself, and being humble about your ability to know it all, are some of the things that you consider to be principles in fact really opinions? Can you put yourself in the shoes of someone holding opposing beliefs and at least appreciate the validity of their opinions?

Extra credit reading

"Humility is essential in being perceived as trustworthy. Do you trust a person who is arrogant, boastful, or narcissistic? When we sense self-grandeur in another person, we often feel an uneasiness in the pit of the stomach—an intuitive warning. Humility is inherent in someone who realizes their strengths and talents are gifts bestowed on them by God. They know these are gifts to be grateful for, not arrogant with...Humble leaders view themselves as blessed and thus revere others and their gifts."

ELLEN CASTRO: *Spirited Leadership*

Something to think about

From humble beginnings spring great achievements; from humble people grow great organizations.

Module #10
The Fourth Cornerstone of Integrity is Stewardship

"You must teach your children that the ground beneath their feet is the ashes of our grandfathers. So that they will respect the land, tell your children that the earth is rich with the lives of our kin. Teach your children that we have taught our children that the earth is our mother. Whatever befalls the earth befalls the sons of earth. If men spit upon the ground, they spit upon themselves...We did not weave the web of life; we are merely a strand in it. Whatever we do to the web, we do to ourselves."

CHIEF SEATTLE

Our goal for this module

To think about stewardship and integrity in both a broader and more intimate sense than usual, weigh the implications of that introspection for our own behaviors, and to inspire changes in those behaviors so that we can do a better job of doing our part of make optimal use of limited resources and pass along a better world to our grandchildren.

> **Glaciers are melting, rainforests are being slashed and burned, oceans are being depleted of fish, and we're using up the globes natural resources as fast as we can, heedless of the deprivations we might be causing our great grandchildren. Resources squandered today—at the personal, organizational, or global level—will inevitably come at a cost to future generations. The real question of integrity is whether we will choose to be effective stewards of the globe, or to be parasites upon the globe.**

Integrity is not just about you—it's about our world

Integrity means honesty and reliability. But it also means wholeness and soundness. Real integrity is more than just a standard of personal behavior. It also requires a broader concern for our resources, our organizations, our earth, and for the generations that will inhabit this fragile planet in the future.

No margin, no mission

The good sisters coined this saying to emphasize the fact that a hospital, like any other organization, must make more than it spends if it is to stay in business to continue its mission of caring for the sick and injured. The same is true for you and me. Make no mistake, I do not believe that whoever dies with the most toys wins, nor do I believe that money is a primary determinant or marker of success. But the nature of my work gives me many opportunities to speak with people about their financial situations. One thing that strikes me is that there is a strong correlation between people saying that money is just not that important to them, and at the same time struggling with big money problems.

In his insightful book *Money and the Meaning of Life*, Jacob Needleman wrote: *"The first practical step that an individual can take to free himself from the thrall of money is not to turn away from it, but to take it more seriously, to study himself with such diligence and concern that the very act of self-study becomes as vivid and intense as the desires and fears he is studying."* Money won't buy you happiness, but the absence of money can certainly buy you unhappiness. Part of being an effective steward is to have a realistic attitude about money, and to make an honest connection between your dreams (to start a business, to travel, to retire to New Mexico, whatever) and the financial resources that will be required to make that dream come true.

Stewardship today for abundance tomorrow

Effective management of resources is not simply a matter of productivity, it is also a matter of integrity. Any resources that are wasted today will somehow diminish the potential for abundance tomorrow. Stewardship takes place at multiple levels—personal, organizational, national, and environmental. Frugality is a debt we owe to our children. Productivity is a debt we owe to our customers. Fiscal responsibility is an obligation that politicians and policy-makers owe to us. Environmental conservation is a debt that we all owe to our grandchildren.

The ultimate homeland security

Robert Redford said this: *"I think the environment should be put in the category of our national security. Defense of our resources is just as important as defense abroad. Otherwise what is there to defend?"* Do you agree with Redford that protecting our environment from ourselves is as important as protecting our nation from foreign enemies? Do you think we're winning that war, or are we losing it?

Consider what Bill Bryson had to say in his masterful book *A Short History of Nearly Everything*: *"It's an unnerving thought that we may be the living universe's supreme achievement and it's worst nightmare simultaneously."* How do you want our species to be remembered? As creation's greatest achievement, or as its worst nightmare? It is a matter of integrity that we mitigate the impact of our impact on this earth, the "worst nightmare" of which Bryson writes.

A great idea: One of the best investments you can ever make is buying an annual pass for the U.S. National Park System. Even if you never visit one of these jewels of our national heritage (which would be a shame), buying an annual pass is still a great investment in one of our nation's greatest assets.

 ## Rules for the Journey

1) Effectively managing resources (waste not, want not) is not merely a matter of prudence and common sense, it's a matter of integrity.

2) Personal stewardship means managing your personal resources so that, should adversity happen, you won't become a burden to your family or our society. Develop a financial plan that helps you achieve financial independence as quickly as possible; this will probably mean making short-term sacrifices.

3) Organizational stewardship requires us to work as efficiently and as productively as possible so that resources can be invested in people (employees and customers). Take to heart the Biblical advice of Ecclesiastes: *"Whatever your hand finds to do, do with all your might."* Go to work with a positive attitude and a willingness to extend yourself for coworkers.

4) Environmental stewardship mandates us to make whatever sacrifices are necessary today so future generations can appreciate the divine world with which we have been blessed, and will have the natural resources with which to build upon the accomplishments of previous generations. Do your part to assure future generations do not suffer through the widely-predicted global environmental crisis by reducing, reusing, and recycling.

Take-home exercise: Give your last credit card a paint job

For many of us, the credit card is the mortal enemy of personal financial stewardship. The primary difference between a credit card and a debit card is that the former allows you to spend money that you do not have. You would be surprised if you knew how many of the people around you are in trouble with credit card debt—and there will be lots more when the house of cards finally tumbles, as it will.

If you don't think you can't get along without having a credit card *"to fall back on"* in case of need, this idea's for you. Cut up all your credit cards but one—your one "fall-back" card. Securely seal that card into a Ziploc bag. Now place that bag into a can of paint and seal it tight. Put the paint can in the far corner of the garage. It will take quite an emergency—something more than the annual sale at Penney's—to drive you to the garage to retrieve your card!!

 ## Extra credit reading

"Values matter because having principles you live by brings you joy, peace, and yes, even wealth... How you handle or mishandle your money tells us who you are and, more important, it tells you who you are. Your priorities, passions, goals, and fears are shown clearly in the flow of your money. Your value system, or lack of one, causes money to flow around you, past you, or to you. When money is in your possession, what you do with it screams loudly who you are."

DAVE RAMSEY: *More Than Enough:*
The 10 Keys to Changing Your Financial Destiny

Something to think about

This land is your land, this land is my land. So, what are you doing to give our land a loving hand?

In his book The Speed of Trust, **Stephen M.R. Covey says that a lack of trust is like a tax that imposes hidden costs on every interaction and every relationship. On the other hand, earning trust means that you can live your life and do your work with fewer rules, fewer contracts, and fewer lawyers. The way you earn that trust is by being a person of integrity.**

Core Action Value #3 is Awareness

If you're not enjoying the journey, the destination will be a disappointment.

Cornerstone #1: Mindfulness

Inner awareness underlies "the miracle of mindfulness" and "the peace of God that passes all understanding" in the world's scriptural literature.

Cornerstone #2: Objectivity

See the world as it really is, not as it used to be, as you wish it were, or as you fear it might be.

Cornerstone #3: Empathy

The ability to read another person's emotions, and to put yourself into their shoes rather than simply reacting out of your own emotions, is the highest form of emotional intelligence.

Cornerstone #4: Reflection

Make sure to make time for yourself—for asking yourself the important questions, and for observing the dominating patterns in your life.

"We resonate with one another's sorrows because we are interconnected. Being whole and simultaneously part of a larger whole, we can change the world simply by changing ourselves. If I become a center of love and kindness in this moment, then in a perhaps small but hardly insignificant way, the world now has a nucleus of love and kindness it lacked the moment before. This benefits me and it benefits others."

JON KABAT-ZINN: *Wherever You Go There You Are*

Module #11
Core Action Value #3 is Awareness

"The only real security in a relationship lies neither in looking back in nostalgia, nor forward in dread or anticipation, but living in the present relationship and accepting it as it is now."

ANNE MORROW LINDBERGH

Our goal for this module

To appreciate the importance, and the power, of awareness for helping us understand what really matters in life, and to fully enjoy the experience of our journey on the human adventure in all its richness and wonder.

> **Strolling along a sidewalk**
>
> **a bump disturbs my dreams**
>
> **My alarm clock**
>
> **did not finish its job**
>
> **– McZen**

Awareness is the key to success and happiness

Awareness is essential to both professional and business success. Your level of awareness will determine the extent to which you appreciate the beauty of the world around you, perceive the opportunities for service and achievement that are always open to someone who is paying attention, and the quality of your interactions and relationships with other people both at work and at home. In the retail world, awareness is the essence of what customers perceive as quality service. In the healthcare environment, awareness profoundly influences both the quality and accuracy of diagnosis and treatment, as well as the patient's perception of the quality of that treatment.

The art of waking up

At its most fundamental level, awareness simply means paying attention, and it has both an inner and an outer dimension. Inwardly, it means being acutely aware of your thoughts, attitudes, and emotions, and not allowing ego, inappropriate emotional reactions, or inauthentic and self-centered ambitions to distort your perception of reality. Outwardly, it means appreciating the beauty of the world around you, and looking past superficialities to really understand what is going on in the events and with the people in your lives.

Manage your temporal attention

One of the most important, and most often overlooked, choices that we make on a day-to-day, hour-to-hour basis is the choice of what we pay attention to. This choice can profoundly influence our moods, our attitudes, and ultimately the kind of results we achieve and the quality of life we live. During your every waking moment, you are giving your mental attention either to the past, the present, or the future. The high school quarterback whose life has gone downhill since the last touchdown is living in the past. The Buddhist monk in orange robes and a begging bowl is diligently striving to live in the present. The inventor and the entrepreneur tend to live in the future.

Of course, for most of us, attention wanders from one time zone to another, often several times a minute. The more consciously and deliberately you manage the allocation of your attention between those three time zones of past, present, and future—and the more selective you are in choosing what you will pay attention to within each of those time zones—the happier and more successful you are likely to be.

Manage your spatial awareness

Have you ever hopped in the car to go somewhere, arrived, and then wondered how you got there? Like McZen's little poem above, your alarm clock didn't finish the job—you went through the drive on autopilot. Another of McZen's little nuggets of wisdom reads:

We each need an alarm clock

tucked in the back of the head

To remind us that being just half-awake

is the same as being half-dead.

One of the best things you can do to wake yourself up is to be simply be more vigilant in observing your surroundings. Instead of burying your nose in the gossip section of the newspaper when you're sitting at the airport, watch the people around you—chances are that they're far more entertaining than the people you'll read about in either *People* or *Entertainment* magazines.

Manage your inner awareness

I'll say more about self-talk in later modules, but for now recognize that much of the inner dialog that goes on between your ears does not nurture you as a person, is not supportive of your dreams, and is not interested in seeing you become your authentic best self. Quite to the contrary, much of that self-talk is the mental equivalent of graffiti, and the first step to overcoming it is to simply pay attention to what it is saying. Catching the little vandal of negativity in the act of spray-painting the walls of your mind is the first step toward rewriting the old scripts that prevent you from breaking out of the self-imposed traps of conformity and mediocrity and becoming the magnificent person you were meant to be.

Enjoy the journey

At one of our *Never Fear, Never Quit* conferences, we had Alan Hobson and Jamie Clarke as speakers. They summited Mount Everest on their third attempt, and shared some very powerful stories (and beautiful slides). One of the most important lessons was this: it took them ten years and they had to raise a total of ten million dollars for their three separate expeditions. When they finally reached the summit, they got to spend just ten minutes at the top of the world before making their descent. Each minute at the top had cost them one million dollars and one year of their lives. As they told our audience, if they had only been in it for the destination, and not for each step of the journey along the way, it wouldn't have been worth the price.

If you're not enjoying the journey, the destination will be a disappointment.

Rules for the Journey

1) Take the advice of Betty Smith (author of *A Tree Grows in Brooklyn*), who said: *"Look at everything as though you were seeing it either for the first or last time. Then your time on earth will be filled with glory."*

2) Devote a bit of time every day to some form of meditation. There are many different forms (Zen, transcendental, centering prayer, walking meditation), and one will feel right to you. You don't need to wear orange robes, and if you can't find half an hour, then give yourself five or ten minutes.

3) Hold your breath. I find that periodically taking and holding a deep breath helps me be more alert and more awake to my surroundings. Don't overdo it—you're not trying to make it into the Guinness book of world records, just enough to stretch your lungs and stretch your mind.

4) Stand on one foot. A friend taught me this exercise as a way of helping me concentrate and stay focused while in meetings. It is very difficult for your mind to wander, not to mention for you to fall asleep, if you are standing on one foot (unless you happen to be a bird).

5) Travel light. The less your sense of self depends upon material possessions, and the less your experience of time depends upon external sensations, the more authentic, the more true to your authentic self, you will be able to be.

 ## Take-home exercise: Carry around a pocket alarm clock

Carry around something in a pocket or in your purse where you will see it and touch it often. A polished worry stone is great for this. (The stone I'm carrying around this week has the words *"Lucky Hiking Stone"* printed on it, with a picture of a boot; I got it at the impulse purchase counter of an airport bookstore.) Whenever it catches your attention, imagine that an alarm clock has just gone off, reminding you to wake up and pay attention to your surroundings. Then look around with new eyes. Imagine that you are in an art museum and whatever is right in front of you has been captured in all its 3-D glory on canvas by the world's greatest artist. Do this several times a day, and you'll begin cultivating the Awareness habit, and a much greater appreciation for the beauty of the world around you.

 Extra credit reading

"To be in the world but not of it means to experience as many things as possible but not to get bogged down or attached to troubles that might impede our human journey. These troubles, which first slow and eventually deaden the pace, include everything from our overinflated egos to the material possessions we covet so much and a host of perceptions in-between. Traveling light isn't just good advice, it's essential wisdom, if we intend to go the full distance on the human journey in comfort and take in as many rich experiences as possible."

BRIAN LUKE SEAWARD: *Quiet Mind, Fearless Heart:*
The Taoist Path through Stress and Spirituality

Something to think about

Why do you think people use the word 'pay' when asking for your attention? Because they are asking you to give them your most precious resource.

Module #12
The First Cornerstone of Awareness is Mindfulness

"One of the tragic things I know about human nature is that all of us tend to put off living. We are all dreaming of some magical rose garden over the horizon—instead of enjoying the roses that are blooming outside our windows today."

DALE CARNEGIE

Our goal for this module

To appreciate the power of mindfulness for personal happiness as well as business, career, and financial success.

Two Buddhist monks were walking along a path when they came across a young woman standing by the bank of a fast-flowing stream. After ascertaining that she needed to cross the stream, one of the monks picked her up and carried her across, then continued on the journey with his companion. As they walked along, the second monk was obviously becoming more and more agitated. At last, he stomped his foot and exclaimed, *"I can't believe you picked that woman up, when we have both made vows to never touch a woman!"* The second monk just smiled and said, *"Brother, I put her down two miles ago; are you still carrying her?"*

Pay Attention

A Zen master was once asked for the secret of a successful life. *"Pay attention,"* he replied. Asked for another secret, he responded, *"Pay attention. Pay attention."* Winston Churchill once said that we first shape our buildings, then our buildings shape us. How much more so with our thoughts and our emotions. Pay attention to your thinking, your moods, and your attitudes, because they are inexorably making you into the person that you are to become. You are not your thoughts, emotions, and attitudes—to become the person you want to be, figure out the ways you need to think and feel in order to be a success, then consciously manage your mental processes to think and feel just that way.

How well you pay attention will determine how successful you are in any career. The doctor or nurse who really pays attention to a patient will pick up little things, make a more discerning diagnosis, and provide more appropriate treatment than the one who simply goes through the motions. The salesperson who pays attention to the subtle clues being given by the customer rather than simply charging ahead, intent on making the sale, will sell more. Everyone wants quality—quality products, quality services, quality jobs, quality lives—but almost no one appreciates that the first step to real quality is simply being awake and paying attention.

> *Attention!*
> *May I have your attention please?*
> *A gift so thoughtlessly requested,*
> *So carelessly given,*
> *So rarely appreciated.*
>
> MCZEN

Lack of mindfulness causes of stress and emotional anguish

When you're feeling emotional pain, it's usually because your consciousness is in a different time zone than that currently being inhabited by your body. Think about it. When you're feeling anger, hatred, guilt, or regret, you are emotionally reacting to something that happened in the past. Likewise, anxiety, worry, doubt, and fear are almost never the result of something here and now, but rather the anticipation of something that might happen in the future. Mindfulness—keeping your conscious mind in the here-and-now—can help you achieve emotional equanimity and spiritual peace. When Buddhists refer to *the miracle of mindfulness*, or Christians talk about *the peace of God that passes all understanding*, what they are really referring to is the state of awareness and gratitude that comes from living in the present.

Slow down on the inside and you can speed up on the outside

It seems that there's never enough time, doesn't it, that we are always in a rush to be somewhere (other than where we are right now) or to be doing something (other than what we're doing right now). Sometimes the best thing you can do to move faster and to get more done in the outside world is to slow down on the inside, take a nice deep breath, and ask yourself this particular *Direction Deflection Question:*

> **Is what I'm about to do right now the most important thing for me to be doing right now? If it's not, what is?**

If you pay attention, you might hear that listening to the chatter of your 2-year-old is more important than getting that report done for the boss. And paradoxically, if you make the time for your child, you just might find that you end up getting the report the boss wants done more quickly as well, because you're attacking it with a renewed spirit (and whose spirit is not renewed after playing with a 2-year-old?).

Listen for the soft voice of Soul through the loud clatter of Ego

I'm intrigued by the battles that are constantly raging within each of us, and with how we can at different times be both our own best friend and our own worst enemy. Listen carefully to your inner self-talk and ask, *"Who's talking? Is it Ego or is it Soul?"* The voice of Ego is usually clamorous and demanding. It wants MORE (of just about everything), and it wants it all NOW. The voice of Soul, by contrast, is gentle and giving. It cares less for things than for people, cares less for status than it does for relationships. Another paradox: while listening to the voice of Ego will usually give you more instant gratification, acting on the voice of Soul will lay a much more solid foundation for your future happiness and success.

Learn from the past, plan for the future, but live in the present

You might have seen the book of mindfulness exercises by Jon Kabat-Zinn entitled *Wherever You Go, There You Are.* For many of us, a more accurate title for the book of our lives would be *Wherever You Go, You're Somewhere Else.* I often see it when I'm giving a speech. There will be someone sitting in the audience who's really not there: their body is in the chair, but there's no one home. Mentally they are in some other time zone. It's important to learn from the past and to plan for the future, but live is lived in the present. As the old saying goes: *Yesterday is a cancelled check, tomorrow is a promissory note, but today is cash!*

Rules for the Journey

1) Past and future are just the bookends—it's in the present that the real story is written. It's a good thing to dream and plan, but you are most likely to succeed if those dreams and plans are based on an accurate and objective assessment of the current reality.

2) Set aside daily "sacred time" for yourself to be devoted to reflection, prayer, meditation, and reading that inspires you.

3) Take up a meditative practice; Zen or transcendental meditation (they are very different approaches), yoga, walking meditation, or other practices can help you enhance your mindfulness, and your joy in the world.

4) Pay attention to what is going on inside of you; your moods and emotions and self-talk can be painful and self-limiting if they are not perceived in a mindful way, but rather just reacted to.

5) Consciously fill open blocks of time with constructive reading and positive thinking so that depressing thoughts are crowded out.

6) Use *Direction Deflection Questions* to help you act with greater awareness in how you spend your time and money, and how you invest your emotional energy.

Take-home exercise: Hawthorne yourself

The Hawthorne Effect refers to the fact that people are more productive when they think they're being observed. Every week, make some small change in your environment that you believe will make you happier or more productive. Imagine that someone you really want to please is watching to see how the change will enhance your productivity. The more strongly you believe that the effect will occur, the more likely it is to do so.

Extra credit reading

"The first step to dealing with feelings is to recognize each feeling as it arises. The agent that does this is mindfulness. In the case of fear, for example, you bring out your mindfulness, look at your fear, and recognize it as fear. You know that fear springs from yourself and that mindfulness also springs from yourself. They are both in you, not fighting, but one taking care of the other."

THICH NHAT HANH: *Peace is Every Step*

Something to think about

"Be Today, See Tomorrow: Keeping your attention in the present is the secret of happiness, and keeping your vision in the future is the key to success."

Module #13
The Second Cornerstone of Awareness is Objectivity

"Shall I tell you what knowledge is? When you know a thing, to know that you know it and when you do not know a thing, to know that you do not know it. That is knowledge."

CONFUCIUS

Our goal for this module

To appreciate the importance of objectivity to success and happiness in work and in life, and to recognize how ego, emotions, ambition and other inner conditions can interfere with an objective assessment of the world around you.

"It was the best of times, it was the worst of times." **That was one of the greatest opening lines ever written, from Charles Dickens' novel *A Tale of Two Cities*. No matter where you are, it is always the best of times and the worst of times, isn't it? It really depends upon what you choose to see. Look around— is it the best of times or worst of times? The answer is *"Yes."***

See the world as it really is

This is my personal definition of objectivity:

To see things as they really are—not as they used to be, as you wish they were, or as you fear they might become, but as they really are.

Moods and emotions can interfere with objective thinking

One of the greatest impediments to objective thinking is your own emotional state. For example, when someone is in a state of high anxiety, problems always seem bigger and more intractable than they really are, while the resources available to deal with those problems seem to be absolutely inadequate when in reality they are probably more than sufficient. Someone acting upon such distorted perceptions can very well end up creating self-fulfilling prophecies of failure and loss.

Be aware of the difference between intuition and gut feel

People often talk about "trusting their gut" and "trusting their intuition" as if these were the same things, but they're not. Gut feel is an inner-directed emotional reaction that says more about you than about the person or event you are reacting to. When you have a gut reaction to someone you've just met, chances are you're not reacting to that person at all, but rather to somebody that person happens to remind you of. Intuition, on the other hand, is outer-directed and substantially non-emotional. It often feels like a gut reaction because a long simmering of facts and figures, observations and conversations, questions and answers suddenly erupt forth in an epiphany, an "ah-hah" moment of enlightenment. Genuine objectivity relies upon having the humility to distrust your gut reactions, the courage to trust your intuition, and the wisdom to know the difference (with appreciation to Reinhold Niebuhr, author of the famous *Serenity Prayer*).

Avoid labels, stereotypes, and first impressions

Despite all kinds of biblical admonitions against it, we humans are a judging race, and are quick to judge other people in the basis of superficial labels, stereotypes, and first impressions. Not only is this unfair to the person you've just met, it can often lead to a harmful self-fulfilling prophecy. If your first impression of someone is that they are untrustworthy, and you react in a way that conveys this, you're likely to end up with a relationship in which neither of you can trust the other.

One way of avoiding this is to use descriptions instead of labels. So, for example, instead of saying that someone is lazy (a label) you might say that they have a hard time meeting deadlines (a description). Notice that in many cases a label implies an irremediable character flaw, whereas a description is more suggestive of a problem amenable to correction.

Be aware for signs of trouble

When we aren't paying attention, we often miss the little signs that can warn of big trouble down the road: the scowl of a valued assistant when given one too many scut work assignments; the slight dip in sales during a quarter when they had been forecast to increase; the body language of a child upon whom a well-intentioned lecture is having an unintended effect. Awareness of small trouble, and the courage to deal with it immediately, can often stave off big trouble later.

Mindfulness means being more involved in the world, not escaping from the world

When they think of meditation and mindfulness, some people visualize bald-headed monks in orange robes living in a far off mountain monastery. Actually, however, a true practice of mindfulness can help you be more consciously present in the everyday world around you. The Buddhist monk Thich Nhat Hanh (author of *Peace is Every Step*) was nominated for the Nobel Peace Prize for his real-world work to end the war in Vietnam.

 ## Rules for the Journey

1) Just because you believe something doesn't make it true. Have the mental flexibility and the spiritual honesty to be objective about your own opinions and beliefs. And as the humorist Artemus Ward said, *"It ain't so much the things we don't know that get us into trouble. It's the things we know that just ain't so."*

1) Try to see yourself as others see you. Whether you do it as part of a formal management process where you work or as a personal initiative on your own, undertaking a 360-degree evaluation will help you gain this objective picture of "you," as seen by the people around you.

2) Have the courage to ask others how you are doing, and the humility to listen to their answers with an open mind.

3) Train yourself to have fewer opinions and more questions. Asking good questions, and then sincerely listening to the responses, is far more conducive to objectivity than is expressing your opinions on the matter.

4) Train your doubt. This was the advice given by the great German poet Rainer Maria Rilke in *Letters to a Young Poet*. When doubt says, *"It will never work,"* train it to instead ask good questions. Like this: *"Whose support do I need to*

make it work, and what can I say that will gain that support?" Or this: *"What do I not know now that if I did know would allow me to move ahead with confidence, and how can I learn what I need to know?"*

5) Change your questions to get at root causes. For example, instead of asking yourself, *"Why does he make me so mad?"* ask yourself this: *"What is it about me that causes his behavior to make me so angry?"*

 ### Take-home exercise: Play reporter

Here's a great way to boost your awareness and enhance your objectivity: pretend that you're a newspaper reporter. Reporters need to be observant, and they need to be objective. I've found that playing "Reporter" is an incredibly helpful exercise, and you will too. You'll be amazed at how effectively this little game can help you keep your eyes sharp, keep your mouth shut, and keep your ears open. In his book *Illusions*, Richard Bach wrote: *"If you will practice being fictional for a while, you will understand that fictional characters are sometimes more real than people with bodies and heartbeats."* Playing Reporter just might help you become more real yourself.

 ### Extra credit reading

"It takes objective thinking to work through challenging situations. Even if there is only an iota of positiveness, you must search to find it. It takes only a match to light of a room. If you sink into the negativity of a situation and start thinking of all the bad things that appear to be happening, the obstacles to your progress will only seem greater. If you focus on only the seeds in a watermelon, you missed the sweetness of the meat."

WALLY AMOS: *Watermelon Magic*

Something to think about

"See the world as it really is—not as it used to be, as you fear it might become, or as you wish it were."

Module #14
The Third Cornerstone of Awareness is Empathy

"The most valuable things in life are not measured in monetary terms. The really important things are not houses and lands, stocks and bonds, automobiles and real state, but friendships, trust, confidence, empathy, mercy, love and faith."

BERTRAND RUSSELL

Our goal for this module

To understand the difference between empathy, sympathy, and commiseration, and to appreciate why empathy is a key attribute of emotional intelligence, as well as being an essential factor for creating meaningful relationships.

We sat together, the forest and I

Merging into silence

Until only the forest remained.

LI PO

Empathy, sympathy, and commiseration

Empathy is the ability to identify with or vicariously experience the feelings, thoughts, or attitudes of another person—to put yourself in their shoes. It is what Daniel Goleman, author of *Emotional* Intelligence, calls "social radar." Empathy differs from sympathy in that it is understanding, without necessarily feeling sorry for the other person. And it is definitely not commiseration, which when broken down into its constituent parts (co–miseration) means "to be miserable together." In fact, commiseration is often nothing more than enabling someone else in their victimhood, affirming their self-pity, and joining them in the swamp of learned helplessness and blame game. That is the antithesis of genuine empathy.

Listen by asking

The essential skill for empathy is listening—not just hearing the words, but really listening for the meaning behind the words, and if possible even the background factors that create that meaning. By really listening, and then asking questions to clarify meaning, you can show the other person that you understand, you care, and for that moment you have your ego under control and are trying to see the world from their perspective. Sometimes, all they want is to be listened to, not to have their problems (or their lives) somehow fixed. When we jump in with an easy solution to a difficult problem, we can convey the message that we really haven't been listening.

Empathy is a guide to doing the right thing

Years ago, I happened to see a small segment of a movie my kids were watching on TV. I don't recall anything about it other than this one scene. A teenager comes waltzing into an electronics store looking for stereo speakers. The gung ho salesman talks him into a set the size of the Washington Monument. Just as the kid is about to write what is probably the biggest check he's ever written, a very pregnant girl comes over and says to him, *"Honey, I'm hungry, can we go now?"* Looking at these young soon-to-be parents, the stereo salesman takes kid back over to the cheapest speakers in the store. *"Trust me, kid, these are just what you need."*

That was empathy in action. The salesman stopped seeing the kid as a commission check with legs, and instead saw a human being with real world responsibilities. Empathy is often not the easiest choice to make (in the case of our salesman, it cost a big commission check), but you must consciously decide to overcome your own ego, ambition, and prejudice (the very word implies pre-judgment) and see the other person as a real live human being—not a commission check with legs, a lost soul to be saved, a strange race to be hated, or an employee to be ordered around. Just a real live human being.

Rules for the Journey

1) Take the advice of Mary Kay Ash and visualize the letters MMFI stenciled on the people's foreheads—for *Make Me Feel Important*; making people feel important, special, and even sacred is the highest form of empathy.

2) One thing I've found particularly helpful is to simply recall the instructions we all learned about crossing a street—stop, look and listen. First, to stop my own inner chatter and desire to quickly fix whatever problem has been presented. Second, to look at the bigger context in which the problem has been presented. And third, to listen for what the person speaking is really trying to say, which might not have much to do with the problem as first presented.

3) One often overlooked blessing is that the tribulations of your life not only make you stronger, they give you a more profound sense of empathy for others who experience similar trials.

4) People in AA adhere to the principle of "mutuality." It's not one drunk helping another because *he* needs help, but rather two drunks helping each other because each needs the help. Without this spirit of mutuality—*we need each other*—empathy can be perceived as being condescending.

5) Let yourself be interrupted. I read somewhere that the best salespeople are in the habit of allowing themselves to be interrupted. The second it appears that their client or prospect is trying to say something, they shut their mouths and listen—really listen. This technique probably sells a lot of cars. It can also go a long way toward resolving arguments—especially those in which you are dead certain that you are right, until you've shut up both your outer and inner voices and listened with genuine empathy to the other person, at which time the flaws in your argument started to reveal themselves.

Take-home exercise: Be a Dionarap

Dionarap is the word paranoid spelled backwards. Being a Dionarap—a backwards paranoid—is one of the surest ways to overcome the fears that stand in the way of genuinely connecting with other people, including fear of rejection, fear of humiliation, and fear of criticism. Convince yourself that people genuinely like and respect you; that when they criticize your ideas or reject your offers, it's nothing personal; and that regardless of what they do or say, they are acting in good faith. If you can do that, you will find the courage to stick your neck out more often and cultivate more meaningful relations.

Too often, because we are hurt by criticism or rejection, a connection is broken, and the relationship stops growing, dead in it's tracks. For the Dionarap, however, criticism and rejection become the opportunity for asking the kind of questions that actually deepen the relationship. And being a Dionarap helps you keep your own ego, and all the suspicions and jealousies it harbors, out of the way when listening to someone else, and thus allows you to be a more genuinely empathetic listener.

Extra credit reading

"The degree to which I can create relationships which facilitate the growth of others as separate persons is a measure of the growth I have achieved in myself."

CARL R. ROGERS: *On Becoming a Person*

Something to think about

We judge ourselves mostly by our intentions, but others judge us mostly by our actions. We judge ourselves mostly by our intentions, but others judge us mostly by our actions. On the other hand, we judge others by their actions while they are judging themselves by their intentions.

Module #15
The Fourth Cornerstone of Awareness is Reflection

"Most true happiness comes from one's inner life, from the disposition of the mind and soul. Admittedly, a good inner life is difficult to achieve, especially in these trying times. It takes reflection and contemplation and self-discipline."

WILLIAM L. SHIRER

Our goal for this module

To appreciate the power and the importance of time devoted to reflection, and to give yourself permission to create time and space for solitude and introspection.

You no doubt know the story of the ugly duckling that grew up to be a beautiful swan. We all have that beautiful swan buried within us, trying to get out and fly. Making the time for reflection is imperative to liberating that inner best self. The most important journeys do not begin with a single step, but rather with a long inward gaze.

Examining your life

The unexamined life is not worth living, said Socrates, and by this he meant that to really fulfill your potential as a human being you must take time to reflect upon what you want, where you are going, and who you are becoming.

Reflection and change

The *I Ching* (Book of Changes) is a classic work of Chinese philosophy that dates back over 3,000 years. Here are two points relevant to someone involved in soul-searching or personal transition:

Just as a well must periodically be taken out of service to be relined, so too there are times when a person must withdraw from the outside world and look inward for a period of soul-searching and soul-building.

Only through daily self-renewal can you maintain your vitality.

Take a few minutes every day to remind yourself of your mission and your goals and the people who are depending upon your success, and to talk back to the little voices that are trying to plant seeds of doubt and despair.

Spend time alone in the desert

Winston Churchill said that anyone who wants to change the world must first spend time alone in the desert; he could well have said the same thing about anyone who wants to make a change in themselves. Especially after a time of trauma—loss of a job, business failure, a fractured relationship—time alone "in the wilderness" can be one of the most important way of enhancing a new self-awareness. In our fast-paced society where busy is good and idle is bad, it's not easy to allow ourselves this time alone. But as Candice Carpenter writes in her book *Chapters*, *"What you have to remember is that you're doing hard work even when you seem to be doing nothing. You're shedding an old skin, the shell you've lived inside, the old way of knowing yourself and letting others know you."* If you pay attention and do the hard work of inner transformation, you will come out of the wilderness stronger and wiser than when you went in.

Learning to see the good, the bad, and the ugly

A common thread running through the literature on meditation and mindfulness is that this is not merely a benign form of relaxation. Quite to the contrary, if taken seriously, the practice can dredge up all sorts of inner demons (see, for example, Charlotte Joko Beck: *Everyday Zen*). True reflection entails honest and forthright observation of your entire character—the good, the bad, and the ugly. When you do this with loving kindness for yourself, a miraculous thing can happen. Instead of crucifying yourself for your failings, or pretending that they don't exist, you can turn them into strengths. It is, for example, this self-compassion that is the first step in transforming the alcoholic or drug addict into a wise counselor.

The Yin and Yang of Soul and Ego

I think of Ego and Soul as the Yang and Yin of personality. It's not that one is bad and the other good; they are complimentary. When I start working on a new book, Ego is motivated by the prospect of fortune and fame; Soul loves the feel of a good pen rolling across a clean sheet of paper and the thought that people I might never meet will be informed and inspired by my words. The combined motivation produced by Ego and Soul together is more powerful than just one would be alone.

There are, of course, times when the two are in conflict. Ego might be secretly pleased to see a perceived rival fall on his face, while Soul will want to help him up, dust him off, and give him a gentle push in the direction of the winners' circle. One thing I've found helpful when dealing with inner conflict is to ask myself, *"who's talking?"* In those situations, I find that I rarely go wrong if I listen to Soul, whereas listening to Ego has gotten me in all kinds of trouble. I've also learned how to distinguish between their voices: Ego is the loud pushy one; Soul is the soft gentle one.

 ## Rules for the Journey

1) No one on their deathbed ever said they wished they'd spent more time watching television, surfing the internet, shopping at Wal-Mart, or pumping nickels into a casino slot machine. Reflection can help you focus your time and energy on the things that really matter.

2) When is the last time you were in a place that was completely free of the sights and sounds of the human civilization noise machine? No television or radio, no passing trucks or ambulance sirens, no crying children or airplanes overhead? Time spent alone in a quiet place for prayer, meditation, and reflection is profoundly good for your soul.

3) Prayer can be an important form of reflection, especially when it is prayer for guidance rather than a prayer of petition. (Gilda Radner asked why it is that if we see someone on his knees talking to God we call it prayer, but if we see that same person on his knees listening to God talk back to him we call it schizophrenia.)

4) Commit yourself to constant renewal, and that always begins with reflection,

with asking questions about what is working, what is not working, what is important, where you want to go and who you want to be.

5) You will never FIND time for Reflection. You must MAKE time. If you don't, the routine and the urgent will perpetually crowd out the time you'd hope to find for the creative and important that are the realm of reflection.

 ## Take-home exercise: Take time for "strategic laziness"

Try to imagine using a hammer to push a nail into a board without ever letting the hammer swing back. It would be difficult, if not impossible, wouldn't it? That's a pretty good metaphor for the person who is always pushing, pushing, and never taking time to recoil and rebuild energy. It is often in moments of "strategic laziness" that we have our greatest ideas, our most profound insights, and where in times of trouble we find the courage to go out and swing the hammer one more time.

 ## Extra credit reading

"As we become more conscious of inherited patterns of thinking, feeling, and acting, we can assess our behavioral legacies and choose not to be controlled by them. As we take charge of our lives, we automatically become more responsible and satisfied at work and more conscious and effective organizational citizens. When the hidden, archetypal power of managers and organizations to act in loco parentis is broken and employees become self-reflecting and self-managing, everyone is finally able to grow up, learn from the past, design their own futures, and be fully responsible for their participation in the present."

KENNETH CLOKE AND JOAN GOLDSMITH:
The Art of Waking People Up:
Cultivating Awareness and Authenticity at Work

Something to think about

Appreciate the two great detachments and the freedoms that they bring: Detachment from material possessions gives you freedom of movement—geographically and professionally; detachment from the opinions of other people gives you freedom of conscience.

Awareness is ultimately the essential skill that determines whether we see the opportunities that life presents to us, how well we relate to the people who come into our lives, and the peace and harmony that we create in our own life and in the lives of others.

Core Action Value #4 is Courage

Fear is a natural, hardwired human emotion. You cannot conquer fear; you cannot drive it out of the workplace. The secret is to make fear your ally and not allow it to be your enemy.

Cornerstone #1: Confrontation

Distinguish between anxiety, fear and worry. Give fear a name and it becomes just a problem; it's easier to solve problems than to conquer fear.

Cornerstone #2: Transformation

The symptoms of terror and exhilaration are identical; it's the interpretation that makes the difference: does fear paralyze you or catalyze you?

Cornerstone #3: Action

Fear is a cowardly emotion; it retreats in the face of determined action. Action transforms fear from emotional molasses to emotional jet fuel.

Cornerstone #4: Connection

Fears shrink when confronted by friends.

"The worst, most damaging learning disability—also by far the most common, affecting 100 percent of the population at one time or another—is fear. Simple fear. Fear of failing. Fear of looking stupid. Fear of being ridiculed or rejected. It starts in school, but it certainly does not end there. It can continue throughout life, holding people back time and again from trying something new, from learning a new skill or trying some advanced technique or starting a fresh career."

EDWARD M. HALLOWELL, M.D.: *Worry: ontrolling It and Using It Wisely*

Module #16
Core Action Value #4 is Courage

"Courage is rightly judged the finest of human qualities because it is the quality which guarantees all the others."

WINSTON CHURCHILL

Our goal for this module

To understand the difference between anxiety, fear, and worry, how these three mental states interact with one another, and to think about practical ways to stand up to the fears that hold us back.

In Ken Kesey's classic book *One Flew Over the Cuckoo's Nest*, Randall Patrick McMurphy is committed to a mental institution, where he makes an important discovery. Most of the men who are there aren't crazy. They're just scared. They're too frightened to face the realities and the responsibilities of the world outside; it's easier for them to pretend to be mentally ill, and to be confined in a prison of their own making. And that is a powerful metaphor for how fear can cause us to construct our own little prisons.

Everyday courage for extraordinary times

We often think of courage in terms of prowess on the battlefield or the playing field. Fortunately, in the world of today most of us are not called upon to perform such acts of physical courage. Rather, what we most need is moral courage. The fears that we need to surmount are not of physical violence, but rather have to do with our relationships and our careers, running out of time and money, and with ultimate spiritual questions such as the meaning of life and the reasons for death. Standing up to these doubts and fears requires a different sort of courage, but summoning that courage is essential if you are to achieve your most authentic goals and dreams, and become the person you are meant to be.

Courage is not the absence of fear

You might have seen t-shirts with the words *"No Fear"* inscribed on them. A more accurate inscription would be *"No Fear, No Courage—Big Fear, Big Courage."* Almost by definition, courage is standing up to fear, not avoiding the experience of fear. Dr. Scott Peck, author of *The Road Less Traveled,* wrote that the absence of fear is not courage—*the absence of fear is brain damage!* Fear is a natural human condition. Our challenge is to harness the emotion for good purpose, and not allow it to interfere with our goals and dreams. Courage means standing up to fear, not eliminating it. That's what courage is, isn't it? Having the strength and determination to overcome your fears and do what you have to do even though you are afraid.

Diagnosing anxiety, fear, and worry

We often use the terms anxiety, fear and worry as though they were interchangeable, but they are in fact three distinct emotional states. Anxiety is a nonspecific state of dread—the black cloud on the horizon. Fear, on the other hand, is specific—you are afraid of *something.* If anxiety is the black cloud in the distance, fear is the raging storm right overhead. And worry is the projection of that fear into the future, the forecast of more raging storms tomorrow. Here's the problem: as Paul Tillich noted in his book *The Courage to Be,* because anxiety is nonspecific dread that has no object, it tries to become fear, because at least fear has an object (the thing you are afraid of), and thus gives you the illusion of control. In other words, the person who is full of anxiety will find much to be afraid of, whether or not those fears are legitimate. It is by reacting to these fears (remember, **the acronym for fear is Fantasized Evidence Appearing Real**) that we end up becoming our own worst enemies.

Anxiety, perception, and performance

In the book *Worry,* Edward Hallowell notes that anxiety increases performance *up to a point,* but that after that point, it causes performance to decline. Norman Dixon's study *On the Psychology of Military Incompetence* sheds some light on why anxiety interferes with performance. Dixon explored the differences between capable and inept military commanders, most of whom had very similar careers until being put into the pressure cooker of the actual battlefield situation for which they had trained. The primary distinction was this:

> *Competent commanders were able to manage their anxiety; incompetent commanders were driven by their anxiety into either paralysis or panic.*

When you are full of anxiety, three bad things happen at a cognitive level:

Memory distortion

When your mind is in the grip of anxiety, your past failures loom large, and seem certain to be repeated, while your past successes feel like distant anomalies that were the result of luck which has now deserted you.

Perception distortion

The high-anxiety person always sees their problems as being bigger and stronger than they really are, and sees his or her own resources as being more limited than they really are.

Vision distortion

The anxious person does not perceive opportunities for audacious action that would not only solve the problem at hand, but could actually bring a stunning turnaround, because he or she can't see through the prison bars of dread.

 ## Rules for the Journey

1) Accept the fact that anxiety, fear, and worry are natural human emotions that everyone feels; don't play the role of victim because you're feeling them, and don't beat yourself up emotionally because you think that if you were stronger, you wouldn't feel them.

2) When you're feeling emotionally distressed, ask yourself whether the predominant emotion is anxiety (nonspecific dread about the uncertain future), fear (acute alarm about a current situation), or worry (anticipating problems in the future).

3) Get the facts. Fear breeds in ignorance and dissipates when you shine the light of knowledge upon it. What do you not know that if you did know would make your fear more manageable, and how can you find it out?

4) Talk back to your fear. When fear is trying to prevent you from taking risks that could in fact eliminate the source of the fear, you need to put on your bravest face, rebut your fears with your bravest affirmations, then fake it till you make it. As Mark Twain said—*act brave, even if you're not, because nobody can tell the difference.*

 ## Take-home exercise: Make fear your ally

Fear is an ally when it alerts you to the fact that you are not prepared for some possible future event. Fear is an ally when it induces you to reach out and ask for help to do that which you cannot do by yourself. Fear is an ally when it prompts you to learn new skills so as to confront the challenges of the future. Fear is an ally when it calls you to stronger faith in yourself. Think about your greatest fears. How can you transform the negative energy of these fears into the positive energy you need for reflection and action?

 ## Extra credit reading

"That's how fear works. First it sends along doubt to soften you up. You begin to doubt whether or not you're doing things right. Then you doubt whether you're doing the right thing. And finally, you doubt whether you're even the right person. Once there is enough doubt, once you stop believing in yourself, then fear knows it can defeat you. Its very cowardice is what makes fear such a treacherous enemy."

JOE TYE: *Never Fear, Never Quit:*
A Story of Courage and Perseverance

Something to think about

F.E.A.R. is the acronym for <u>F</u>antasized <u>E</u>vidence <u>A</u>ppearing <u>R</u>eal. It also happens to be the acronym for <u>F</u>abulous <u>E</u>xcuse for <u>A</u>voiding <u>R</u>esponsibility.

Module #17
The First Cornerstone of Courage is Confrontation

"You gain strength, courage and confidence by every experience in which you really stop to look fear in the face."

ELEANOR ROOSEVELT

Our goal for this module

Make the internal commitment to stand up to our fears with courage and to do the things we're afraid to do but which we know should be done.

In his book *The Anatomy of Courage*, Lord Moran (private physician to Winston Churchill) wrote: *"Courage... is a cold choice between two alternatives, the fixed resolve not to quit; an act of renunciation which must be made not once but many times by the power of will."* It takes courage to chart your own path, to set audacious goals where success is uncertain, and to overcome the doubts and fears that stop those who are less courageous dead in their tracks.

See fear for what it really is

As in treating illness, so too with overcoming fear—the first step is diagnosis; you can't fight what you can't see. And as in medical care, a missed diagnosis can result in the wrong treatment, causing contrary and potentially adverse outcomes. For example, if you diagnose yourself as having fear of failure, but at a subconscious level what you really fear is success, each step you take to overcome the fear of failure could actually make things worse, since it brings you that much closer to the success that is the real cause of your anxiety. Fear can be a terrible enemy—can be your worst enemy. And since it pays to know your enemy, let's take a closer look.

Fear is a Coward

It will attack you only when your strength falters. Like most cowards, though, it will retreat when you confront it bravely. Reminding yourself that you're ultimately strong enough to cope with whatever life brings will help you keep fear at bay.

Fear is a Liar

It will take a bundle of apparent facts, each of which might be true alone, and weave them into a picture that is totally false. By accepting fear's threatening picture of the world, you become a participant in a fraud—a fraud in which you are also the victim.

Fear is a Prison

Fear is like the Great Wall of China—far better at keeping you trapped inside your self-limiting little comfort zone than at preventing frightening things from entering into your life. Fear can immobilize you more totally than the iron bars in a prison door.

Fear is a Thief

Fear can steal your freedom to act, your desire to succeed, your willingness to take risk, and your capacity to care. It is also the source of much procrastination and apparent laziness, and a lethal barrier to creativity.

Fear is a Killer

Any harm that can be caused to you by direct violence you can also cause to yourself by your reaction to fear; it can destroy your health and even take your life.

Fear Is a Reaction, Courage Is a Decision!

Metaphors can cause anxiety or promote courage

The mind, wrote theologian Paul Tillich, is a factory that produces fear. We don't do this deliberately, or even consciously, but what we allow to play in the theaters of our minds substantially determines whether we are paralyzed by fear or galvanized by courage. As a way of trying to simplify and comprehend the world, the human mind naturally uses metaphors. Unfortunately, the way we use metaphors can produce great anxiety. One way to change your life is to change the metaphors you use to describe your life. Think about these common metaphors. Can you see how, even if you think you're just shooting off a quick throwaway line, your subconscious mind would react with a mini-panic attack?

I'm up against a deadline (the line where you die), my back is against the wall (that's where they put someone before a firing squad), I'm hanging in there (hanging by the fingernails? by the neck?), I'm behind the eight ball (the loser's position in a game of pool). And you wonder why you're feeling stressed out?

There was blood all over the floor, he got cut off at the knees, she got handed her head on a platter, he sure got shot down—these common metaphors conjure up subconscious mental images of horrific and graphic violence, and inevitably create stress and anxiety when they are used in the workplace.

My head is killing me, I'm out of gas, dead in the water, dead on my feet, dying for a cigarette (that one might actually not be a metaphor), I'm fried, I'm toast, I'm burned out—is it any wonder you're so often exhausted, if those are the metaphors you're using to describe your feelings?

On the other hand, positive metaphors can be a source of encouragement and empowerment. Consider, for example, these:

This will be a walk in the park, easy as pie, piece of cake, could do it in my sleep; the plan is rock-solid, gold-plated, bullet-proof; I'm on top of the world, feeling like a million dollars, could walk through walls.

Can you see how these metaphors are saying something very different to the subconscious mind? Think back over your conversations of the past week or so. What metaphors have you used, and how do you think the people to whom you were speaking might have interpreted these metaphors? What metaphors have you used in your own inner dialog?

 ## Rules for the Journey

1) Fear is a bully which you need to stand up to if you are going to achieve your most important goals; it is also a coward that will back down in the face of courageous determination.

2) If you give fear a name, it becomes just a problem; it's easier to solve problems than it is to conquer fear.

3) Bolster your courage by replacing vague generalizations with specific statements of fact.

4) Fear is the most toxic of emotions; it can be a prison more constraining than any iron bars, but it's hard for fear to imprison you when you're laughing. Make a list of some of the things you can do to be more spontaneous, more outrageous, more adventurous, and more of the fun-loving person that you were as a child. Then pick one or two and actually go out and do them!

5) Watch the metaphors that you use to describe (and define) yourself and your circumstances, and replace fearful and disempowering metaphors with metaphors that are encouraging and empowering (and frankly, more likely to be true).

 ### Take-home exercise: Be a Dionarap (take two)

After defining the clinical condition of paranoia, Webster's Unabridged Dictionary goes on to define the everyday variety as "*baseless* or *excessive* suspicion of the motives of others" (emphasis added by me, and for a good reason!!). Being paranoid can be seriously harmful to your happiness, and to your success. Consider this about two of the predominant fears in the world of business—fear of rejection and fear of failure.

> *People are not afraid of rejection—they are afraid that <u>someone</u> will reject them (in other words, they are paranoid).*

> *People are not afraid of failure—they are afraid of the embarrassment that might be caused by what other people think of the fact that they failed (in other words, they are paranoid).*

When you make negative assumptions about other people (they will reject me, they will laugh at me if I fail), those assumptions will quite likely influence your attitudes and your behaviors. In other words, your negative assumptions about other people can bring about a self-fulfilling prophecy. If you expect to be rejected, the way you present yourself could telegraph that expectation, and as a result you could end up with that rejection letter. The solution is to do a complete 180-degree shift in attitude, to go from being a paranoid to being a Dionarap (don't try to look that word up in Webster's—I made it up).

Dionarap is the word paranoid spelled backwards. Being a Dionarap—a backwards paranoid—is one of the surest ways to overcome the fears that stand in the way of genuinely connecting with other people, including fear of rejection, fear of humiliation, and fear of criticism. Convince yourself that people genuinely like and respect you; that when they criticize your ideas or reject your offers, it's nothing personal; and that regardless of what they do or say, they are acting in good faith. If you can do that, you will find the courage to stick your neck out more often and cultivate more meaningful relations. Too often, because we are hurt by criticism or rejection, a connection is broken, and the relationship stops growing, dead in it's tracks. For the Dionarap, however, criticism and rejection become the opportunity for asking the kind of questions that actually deepen the relationship.

 Extra credit reading

"He who has conquered doubt and fear has conquered failure. His every thought is allied with power, and all difficulties are bravely met and wisely overcome... Thought allied fearlessly to purpose becomes creative force."

JAMES ALLEN: *As A Man Thinketh*

Something to think about

Fear is a reaction, courage is a decision.

Module #18
The Second Cornerstone of Courage is Transformation

→ →

"To be courageous...requires no exceptional qualifications, no magic formula, no special combination of time, place and circumstance. It is an opportunity that sooner or later is presented to us all."

JOHN F. KENNEDY

Our goal for this module

To recognize that fear is nothing more than emotional energy, and that by our conscious choice we can transform that energy from a negative emotional state that holds us back in cowering paralysis into a positive emotional state that catalyzes us to take action and move forward.

You know the story of the Ugly Duckling, don't you? The ugly little duckling grew up to become a beautiful swan. That's transformation at its best! We each face the same challenge in our emotional lives: how to transform ugly, and often paralyzing, fear into beautiful, and always galvanizing, courage. Remember, fear is a reaction; courage is a decision. Decide for courage by transforming your fears.

Fear is emotional energy—so is courage

Fear and courage are opposite sides of the same coin. There is no courage without fear. One of the greatest challenges in life is learning the skill of transforming fear into courage. Think about this: the physical symptoms of terror and exhilaration are identical: sweaty palms, racing pulse, wide eyes, shallow breathing. The only distinction between the two states is how we define the symptoms (which is why people like to ride roller-coasters: controlled terror!). That is a great metaphor for transforming fear into courage.

Act "as if" you had courage

The most powerful precept in the entire self-help literature is the "AS IF" principle. Two thousand years ago, Jesus said that when you pray, you should pray *as if* your prayers had already been answered. More recently, Winston Churchill said that we should act *as if* it were impossible to fail. When you look in the mirror, see a face that is optimistic, cheerful, and determined—*as if* that face belonged to a person who was already sitting on top of the world. You've heard it said that life is not a dress rehearsal. Well, in at least one important respect, life *is* a dress rehearsal: the way you act today is your rehearsal for tomorrow. If you walk around today with a long face that says to the rest of the world that you're defeated and hopeless, bitter and angry, that's what you will be tomorrow: defeated and hopeless, angry and bitter. On the other hand, if your face conveys an expression of hope and optimism, if it is set with determination to prevail despite whatever odds might be arrayed against you, you can be certain you will succeed—though you might need a fair bit of rehearsing before you're ready for prime time.

Distinguish between fear and risk

Whenever I speak with groups of sales professionals, I ask them what they perceive to be the major barrier to success in their field. The answer is always the same: fear of rejection. Of course, nobody likes to be rejected. As Steven Pressfield points out in his book *The War of Art: Winning the Inner Creative Battle*, the fear of being rejected goes back to our caveman days, when to be rejected by the tribe meant isolation and almost certain death. This innate fear was intensified over the centuries by church organizations that coupled excommunication with the threat of eternal damnation. The fear of rejection is deeply imprinted in our psyches. But in today's world, that fear is not rational, because in most cases the *risk* associated with rejection is virtually zero. When someone says no to a salesperson, he is absolutely no worse off than he was before the "rejection." In fact, if he has the proper perspective he's actually better off, because the prospect's lack of interest can guide him toward changes he might need to make in his product or his pitch. The fear is high but the risk is zilch!

Paradoxically, many of us are not sufficiently afraid of some of the *real* risks in life. For example, spending evenings being a vegetable on the couch in front of the tube is a definite risk factor for early death from heart disease (if not even earlier death from terminal boredom), but you don't see people having mini-panic attacks before they go plop down on the sofa. Likewise, reading *People* magazine instead of a good book on personal finances increases the risk that the reader will retire to a life of poverty and privation, yet you don't see people getting sweaty palms and short of breath as they waste their time on tabloid gossip, even though the risk is quite real.

Follow your anxiety

There is good news about anxiety—it can guide you to your meant-to-be path in life. In *Finding Serenity in the Age of Anxiety*, Robert Gerzon says that anxiety can actually be a guide to our greatest strengths, our greatest joys, and our life's true calling. He says: *"It is our deepest desires that can arouse our greatest apprehension—for what if we should try, really try with all our heart, and fail?"* That one sentence says so much, doesn't it? It explains why so many would-be writers freeze the moment they sit down in front of a keyboard. It explains why so many now-successful actors, debaters, and public speakers were once terrified of standing in front of an audience. And it explains why so many people find so many excuses to avoid "following their bliss," in the memorable phrase of Joseph Campbell, because standing between them and the bliss of their calling is the anxiety of transforming, of stretching, of reaching and growing.

 ## Rules for the Journey

1) One of the chief challenges in life is to overcome the old memories that hold you back from achieving what you are capable of achieving, from becoming the person you were born to be.

2) Recognize that both fear and courage are contagious, and that the best way for you to gain courage is to share it with others, even if you think you don't have it.

3) Transform the negative energy of fear into the positive, catalytic energy for productive action. Courage without energy is little more than a good intention; energy without courage is more likely to run away than it is to stand and fight.

4) Think of some of the things that cause you the greatest fear—such as, perhaps, the fear that you might lose your job, you might go broke, you might wake up one morning and find that nobody likes you, whatever. Now, identify the underlying problems and write about some of the things you could do in order to solve those problem.

5) *Word are Powerful!* Be careful to distinguish between verbs, adjectives, and nouns. To have failed (verb) at keeping a job, or to have been part of a failing (adjective) business, does not make you a failure (noun).

6) Think of self-defining metaphors that are holding you back, probably without you even being aware of it (*"I'm a chicken"* or *"I'm hanging in there"*); how can you transform these into empowering metaphors?

 ## Take-home exercise: Identify your irrational fears

One cause of anxiety is the irrational fears that we harbor, often from long-forgotten childhood experiences. I once saw a bumper sticker that read:

> ***"Buckle Up! It makes it harder for the aliens to suck you out of your car."***

That's funny—unless you truly are afraid of being sucked out of your car by aliens, in which case you probably need a level of help beyond that provided by this *Guided Self-Coaching Course on The Twelve Core Action Values*. While you might not be afraid of being sucked out of your car by alien invaders, chances are that you have other irrational fears. Perhaps you don't swim in the ocean for fear of sharks, even though your chances of being struck by lightning are far greater than your chances of being eaten by a shark. Or maybe the mere thought of picking up a perfectly harmless garter snake causes you to shake in your shoes.

Most of us have irrational fears that might on the surface seem perfectly rational—fear of poverty in the land of plenty (where the closest most people come to real starvation is the pizza delivery guy showing up late); fear of poor health in the age of medical miracles; fear of death at a time when historical longevity records are being shattered. Some of these irrational fears can be perfectly harmless (after all, most of us don't pay any sort of penalty for not swimming in the ocean or avoiding garter snakes), but others can be terribly confining. The person who is terrified of rejection will never ask; the person who is terrified of failure will never try.

The first step to conquering irrational fears is simply to identify them and to shine the cold light of rational thought upon them. The second step is often to find the humor in them (*"can you imagine, I used to keep my car windows up on a hot day for fear of being sucked out the window by alien invaders"*). The third step is often to confront the fear head-on—going for that swim or picking up that snake. Of course, some fears really are warranted—make sure that it's a garter snake and not a coral snake, and that there's a lifeguard on the beach.

Extra credit reading

"Since life is frightening, without courage it would be unbearable. Courage rallies our spirits dozens of times daily. But even when we face down our fears—and you would be amazed how often we succeed in doing precisely that—we are still more conscious of our cowardice than of our courage. We feel the fear over which we triumph at the very moment of triumph itself, yet rarely do we actually feel courage. We rally to it's call, but we don't feel it. What courageous people feel is fear: It is what soldiers feel. And expectant mothers. And awkward teenage boys when they ask a girl out on a date. In fact, it is what all of us feel in a hundred little ways every day of our lives. We feel frightened and demonstrate courage."

FORREST CHURCH: *Freedom from Fear*

Something to think about

At one point or another, people must choose: the certainty of misery or misery of uncertainty. Resparking the spirit of adventure in your life can help you deal with uncertainty with courage and determination.

Module #19
The Third Cornerstone of Courage is Action

"Inaction breeds doubt and fear. Action breeds confidence and courage. If you want to conquer fear, do not sit home and think about it. Go out and get busy."

DALE CARNEGIE

Our goal for this module

To appreciate that without action, courage is nothing more than a good intention, and to make the commitment to do the things that need to be done in order for us to achieve our most authentic goals and become our most authentic selves, even though we might be afraid.

Four men are sitting in a bar sharing horror stories about their awful jobs, each striving to outdo the other with the indignities of their work. Finally, they decide that they're all going to quit and start a business together. Now, how many entrepreneurs are sitting at the table in that barroom? Answer: Zero. The next day, they all went back to their odious jobs. Merely making a decision means nothing until it is acted upon.

Action is where the rubber hits the road

In the previous modules, we covered techniques for diagnosing anxiety, fear, and worry and for transforming the negative energy of these emotions into positive, catalytic energy for constructive change. When it comes to courage, though, action is where the rubber hits the road. Action is:

- The key difference between wishful thinking (which is hoping for something and waiting for it to happen) and positive thinking (which is expecting something and working to make it to happen).

- The coin with which one purchases self-confidence and genuine self-esteem.

- The catalyst that transforms hope into expectation.

◻ The foundation upon which most good habits are built (while inaction is the source of many bad habits).

Action, as the late Og Mandino once wrote, transforms the lion of terror into an ant of equanimity. In previous modules I've said that fear is a reaction; courage is a decision. That's true, but it does not go far enough. The decision itself is not really courage until it is acted upon.

I will do the things I'm afraid to do, but which I know should be done. Sometimes this will mean asking for help to do that which I cannot do by myself.

(Wednesday's Promise of *The Self-Empowerment Pledge*)

Taking action means willingness to take risks

In their book *Whoever Makes the Most Mistakes Wins*, Richard Farson and Ralph Keyes argue that *"the world belongs to those who don't let anxiety about screwing up keep them from moving forward. Those who are too afraid to make a mistake work for those who aren't."* To act is to risk, and to risk is to eventually fail. Unfortunately, in our risk-averse world, failure has gotten a bad name. Because people are afraid to fail, they are afraid to act; because they fail to act, they fail to learn and grow, which is the ultimate failure. Farson and Keyes point out that the most successful organizations, and the most successful individuals, generally have a track record of "failure" (and learning from that perceived failure) that leads up to the success for which they are recognized.

Mastering the performance-anxiety curve

In his book *Worry*, Edward M. Hallowell describes the performance-anxiety curve, which *"shows that as anxiety increases, performance improves, up to a point. Beyond that point, as anxiety continues to increase, performance declines."* Hallowell cites studies showing that effective entrepreneurs and business leaders might worry a lot, but that their worry has two distinct characteristics. First, it is focused on achievement of goals, not concern for personal advancement or the opinions of others. Second, it precipitates action that reduces the cause of the worry, thereby freeing the leader's attention to focus on some other worry. Take a look at the Performance-Anxiety Curve graph below. To the left of the "optimum level" point of anxiety, performance increases because it stimulates effective action. But to the right of that high point, performance drops off precipitously.

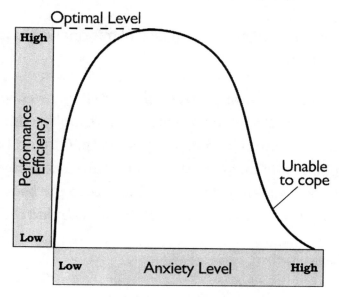

The Performance-Anxiety Curve

Your challenge is to recognize anxiety for what it is as soon as you start to feel it. Is it an early warning that you need to start getting ready for some future event, or is it simply an out-of-place emotion, perhaps caused by the fact that you haven't been getting enough sleep? This will help you either transform that generalized anxiety into a specific fear, or dismiss it. Once you've given fear a name and turned it into a problem, the next step is to specify the actions you can take to work on solving that problem. Then, that catalytic anxiety can give you a sense of urgency and a jolt of energy if you use it effectively.

 ## Rules for the Journey

1) Action is the difference between positive thinking (*expecting* something and working to make it to happen) and wishful thinking (*hoping* for something and waiting for someone else to make it happen).

2) *"To see what is right and not to do it is cowardice,"* Confucius is quoted as saying in *The Analects*. We usually know what needs to be done in any given

situation—the challenge is often getting ourselves to do it.

3) Dare most when times are darkest; it is precisely when things seem most hopeless that positive thinkers make great things happen.

4) Fear and anxiety are magnified by a lack of information; use research to shed a light on your fears.

5) Keep moving. Feeling out of control—of yourself, your environment, your future—can be terribly frightening. One of the simplest things you can do to re-exert a sense of control is to move. Just move. Go for a brisk walk or a jog. Pick up the phone and make a call. We know from the science of psychoneuroimmunology that not only does the mind talk to the body, the body talks to the mind. Action is a message from the body to the mind that things are under control.

 ### Take-home exercise: Draw your own Performance-Anxiety Curve

Think about something that is now causing you anxiety, or is likely to in the near future. Do you have a performance review coming up at work, or are you about to go in and ask for a raise? Are you a salesperson with a directory of contacts and a telephone waiting for you at your desk? Are you a writer about to sit down to a blank yellow pad? If you answer yes to these questions or any like them, the chances are good that you're about to feel anxiety. Draw a curve like the one above, then mark the point of your current anxiety level. If you're too far to the left, perhaps you're being too complacent about the upcoming challenge. If you're too far to the right, you might cross (or already have crossed) over the point where your effectiveness will diminish. Imagine how you'll be feeling, and where you'll be on this curve, as you approach the event that's causing you anxiety. Taking the time now to anticipate these feelings will help you recognize them as they arise and take effective action to counter them.

Extra credit reading

"The person who is free from fear does something [rather than just complain]. He makes conscious choices. He is proactive rather than passive. He doesn't let life happen to him. He makes his life happen. He doesn't complain. He captures the moment and makes the very best of it. He sees everything as an opportunity to learn something new, share something about himself, or make a request."

RHONDA BRITTEN: *Fearless Living: Live Without Excuses and Love Without Regret*

Something to think about

The difference between courageous and crazy is often evident only long after the fact.

Module #20
The Fourth Cornerstone of Courage is Connection

"Two are better than one, because they have a good return for their work: If one falls down, his friend can help him up."

ECCLESIASTES 3:9-10

Our goal for this module

To appreciate how vital human connection is in the courage equation, and to consider some of the ways that we can connect and create a greater spirit of community and fellowship.

Did you see the movie *Cast Away* with Tom Hanks? The character he played was marooned on a desert island with only a volleyball to keep him company. By movie's end, "Wilson" had become his debate partner, his best friend, his soulmate. The need for human-to-human connection is so deeply ingrained in our genes that we will manufacture another person out of thin air (or out of a volleyball) if the real thing is not available. Not only is connection key to human happiness and success, it is also the most important way to bring down the "silo walls" that divide our organizations.

Caring is the root of courage

"Caring is the root of courage; if you care enough about something, you will find the courage to do what needs to be done." I think about that line from *Never Fear, Never Quit* whenever I see a redwing blackbird chasing a crow or a hawk away from its nest. The bigger birds outweigh the redwing by ten or twenty times, but still the little bird finds the courage to protect its home. There's a great lesson there. Whatever it is you should be doing or want to be doing but are not doing because you're afraid, remind yourself of why you care. If you're not writing the book that burning up inside of you, or not making the calls that are essential to achieving your sales goals, for fear of rejection, then remind yourself of why you care. *You're*

afraid precisely because you care! Focusing on the care, and not on the fear, is often the first step to overcoming the inner barriers that have you stalled.

We need to rebuild the spirit of community

A while ago I was speaking with a nurse from the Philippines. We were talking about community, and what she said was heartbreaking. She said that where she lived in the Philippines, people didn't have much money. *"But at the end of the day,"* she said, *"we gather in the square with transistor radios and we talk and dance and sing. Walk through any community in America, and you don't see singing and dancing—you see people watching TV or mowing their lawns, all alone. You have money, but your poverty is more real than that of my people who have no money."* Think about the place where you work. Is there music playing, are people singing and dancing (at least in the metaphorical sense)? Do coworkers support each other when things get stressful? Is there a spirit of cooperation and collegiality between departments? Or is the place divided by walls of indifference and fear?

Distrust first impressions and stereotypes

Most of us pride ourselves on the ability to be a good judge of other people based on our gut reactions. Most of us are wrong. First impressions tend to be based upon superficial exterior attributes and a person's social and material status. Listening to your gut can prevent you from really getting to know people who seem to be different from you, and unnecessarily limit your circle of friends to include only people who are pretty much just like you. We tend to judge other people by what we think they have already done, not by what they say they would like to do. On the other hand, we tend to judge ourselves by our intentions, and wish other people to do likewise. Keep this in mind the next time you're about to come down hard on someone for not keeping a commitment, or feeling resentful at someone for not giving you the benefit of the doubt when you haven't kept yours.

Dark days can create best friends

If you have ever attended a support group meeting of any kind, you know that most people leave in a better frame of mind than when they came. Their problems are not solved, but they gain hope, wisdom, and courage from others that helps them better cope with their predicament. Imagine if that were our commitment in the workplace—that at the end of a stressful day, we would not allow anyone to go home worse than they came in, probably to dump all of that negativity on members of their family. Imagine a workplace where failure is met with sympathy and hugs rather than fear and recrimination; where the response to a costly mistake is to make sure it doesn't happen again to someone else; where today's victim becomes tomorrow's teacher and mentor; and where the depths of every setback are plumbed for meaning, lessons, and opportunities for personal growth. I'll bet your first thought was you'd like to work there, and your second was that such an organization would be destined for greatness.

 ## Rules for the Journey

1) *"Reach out in the darkness and you might find a friend,"* went the hit song from the sixties; fear breeds in isolation while connection inspires courage.

2) Caring is the root of courage; remind yourself of who you care for, of why you care. That knowledge, the why and the who of your caring, will point you in the direction of what you must do to effectively express that caring, and give you the courage to do it.

3) Fear and courage are contagious; take to heart advice of Robert Louis Stevenson: *"Keep your fears to yourself, but share your courage with others."*

4) "Silo effect" is a metaphor used to describe the gulf that separates divisions within an organization ("division"—the very word implies separation); one of the challenges to "drive fear out of the workplace" is to bring down the silo walls, enhance communication, and promote a spirit of community.

5) Listening to first impressions can prevent you from really getting to know

people who seem to be different from you, and unnecessarily limit your circle of friends to include only people who are pretty much just like you.

 ## Take-home exercise: Seek a mentor and be a mentor

Speak long enough with someone who's successful in any field, and they are likely to point to the influence of some coach, teacher, or mentor in their past. One of the things you can do to enhance you own courage connection is seek out people who can serve as mentors for you. This could be an informal relationship, as in seeking advice from people who have been successful at accomplishing something you would like to do. It could also be a more formal relationship with a professional coach. As you progress in your relationship with the people you look up to as mentors, begin to be on the lookout for others whom you can help by being a mentor yourself.

 ## Extra credit reading

"Connectedness is the most powerful antidote we have to toxic worry at work. Conversely, disconnectedness is the most common cause of toxic worry at work. Connectedness means simply a feeling of being a part of something larger than yourself. A family. A neighborhood. A cause. Or, in the business world, a company or corporation. Connectedness seems to have broken down in America over the past fifty years."

EDWARD M. HALLOWELL, M.D.: *Worry: Controlling It and Using It Wisely*

Something to think about

The Course In Miracles says that the opposite of love is not hate, it is fear. If that is true, it also stands to reason that love can also be the antidote to fear. In the words of a song by the contemporary musical group Morcheeba, *"fear can stop your loving, love can stop your fear."*

You probably did not take a course on courage in school, which is too bad since courage is a defining characteristic of personal and professional success. Fortunately, courage is not a genetic trait but rather is a learned skill. And the more you work on developing that skill, the more successful you will be.

Core Action Value #5 is Perseverance

Every magnificent accomplishment was once the "impossible" dream of a dreamer who simply refused to quit when the going got tough. If courage is a decision, perseverance is making that decision day after day after day.

Cornerstone #1: Preparation

Adversity can be anticipated in general but not in specific, so prepare the way a fire department trains—getting ready for whatever might happen.

Cornerstone #2: Perspective

Whether it is the best of times or the worst of times depends upon what you choose to see. Choose a positive perspective.

Cornerstone #3: Toughness

Internalize a spirit of contrarian toughness by internalizing the TGAoT (Thank God Ahead of Time) philosophy for dealing with adversity.

Cornerstone #4: Learning

Life's most important lessons, greatest opportunities, and most cherished friendships are most often formed during times of adversity.

"The clear-cut assessment of many successful individuals anchors around setbacks and rejection. Make no mistake about it: Victories that come easy are cheap. Achievement owes its growth to the striving of the will, the encounter with fear, the ever-present danger of failure. He who has never failed has never succeeded."

DENNIS P. KIMBRO: *What Makes the Great Great: Strategies for Extraordinary Achievement*

Module #21
Core Action Value #5 is Perseverance

"I do not think there is any other quality so essential to success of any kind as the quality of perseverance. It overcomes almost anything, even nature."

JOHN D. ROCKEFELLER

Our goal for this module

To appreciate that perseverance is the key to successful achievement of any goal that's worth pursuing, and to make a commitment to persevere in the pursuit of our own authentic goals and dreams.

When John Wooden joined UCLA as head basketball coach in 1948, the school didn't even have a proper basketball facility. It would be sixteen years—all if them housed in what was known as *"the B.O. Barn"*—before Wooden's UCLA team won the first of ten national titles between 1964 and 1975, an accomplishment that may well never be equaled. What would have happened if the UCLA administration had given up on Wooden, or if he had given up on himself, in 1963? After all, isn't fifteen years enough time to see whether a coach has it in him to take a team all the way to the top? Right—nothing.

Perseverance is Courage that Endures

Perseverance follows naturally upon courage—it takes courage to start something, it takes perseverance to not quit when the inevitable obstacles and setbacks arise. In the modules for Core Action Value #4, Courage, I said that fear is a reaction, while courage is a decision. Given that, here's a pretty good definition for perseverance:

Perseverance is making the decision to act with courage day after day, despite the obstacles and setbacks along the way.

Thomas Edison once said that people would be appalled if they only knew just how close they were to success when they quit. Anyone who's ever run a race knows that the pain increases the closer you get to the finish line. It's when the pain is greatest that an extra spark of determination will push you across the finish line; it's when you most feel like quitting that you must reach deep within and find that extra measure of energy, and the strength of character, that you never suspected to be within you. Perseverance truly is the fuel that transforms the dreams of today into the reality of tomorrow.

The Laws of Adversity

Adversity is bitter medicine, but like most bitter medicine, it serves to make us better. As the Arab metaphor puts it, all sunshine makes a desert (and with the rain comes flowers and rainbows). Without adversity, there would be no need for perseverance—but with perseverance, adversity becomes an opportunity for personal growth. And here are its laws:

- We learn and grow more from our setbacks than we do from our successes. Successfully overcoming the adversity of today prepares you for bigger challenges and accomplishments in the future.

- Surviving adversity is a great way to build self-confidence, and to give you a more positive perspective on future adversity ("if we made it through *that* we can survive anything!").

- Adversity helps prevent hubris, arrogance, and complacency.

- When things aren't working, it forces you to look for more creative solutions.

- What you've fought to gain you'll fight to keep and visa versa—easy come, easy go. Past adversity translates into future tenacity.

- There is opportunity hidden in every adversity if you have the strength and courage to search for it and to pursue it when you've found it.

- Without the valleys, you won't appreciate the mountains.

- Adversity keeps teaching—it provides great stories for the grandchildren! Your setbacks can, if you're committed to learning from them and teaching about them, be the source of great learning for others.

Apparent versus real failure

In *Frontiers of Management*, Harvard Business School professor Rosabeth Moss Kanter wrote that *"everything can look like a failure in the middle."* Ain't it the truth! We remember our greatest leaders not so much for their successes as for their perseverance through apparent failure in the middle: Moses in the desert, Jesus at his trial, Joan of Arc at Orleans, Washington at Valley Forge, Churchill during the blitz, Helen Keller in the silent darkness, Nelson Mandela in prison. The leaders who truly inspire us are those who refuse to succumb to apparent failure, because they recognize it is only failure if they quit.

 ## Rules for the Journey

1) Obstacles are not optional, and though they cannot be predicted with precision, they can be anticipated in general; the secret is to prepare in much the same way that a fire department prepares for the next fire.

2) Every successful athletic coach knows this truth: spectacular success is always preceded by unspectacular preparation. No football team ever won a game because of the pre-game pep rally—victory is always founded upon a solid base of discipline and preparation.

3) No adversity comes your way that does not have hidden within it the seeds of a future blessing; it is your challenge to find and capitalize upon that proverbial silver lining.

4) The bigger your dream, the greater will be the challenges you'll face in transforming the dream of today into the reality of tomorrow.

Take-home exercise: Transform a complaint into a blessing

Anything that you complain about can be transformed into a blessing. Anything. Does your back hurt? Be thankful for ibuprofen. Just lost a job? Consider yourself fortunate that you don't live in Bangladesh. Motivational speaker Les Brown says that any morning he wakes up and doesn't see a chalk line etched around his body, he knows it will be a great day! If you wake up tomorrow and there's a chalk line around your body, start complaining. Otherwise, turn those complaints into blessings and focus your attention and energy on the positive contributions you can make.

Extra credit reading

"Persistence is probably the single most common quality of high achievers. They simply refuse to give up. The longer you hang in there, the greater the chance that something will happen in your favor. No matter how hard it seems, the longer you persist the more likely your success."

JACK CANFIELD: *The Success Principles*

Something to think about

Every magnificent accomplishment was once the impossible dream of a dreamer who simply refused to quit when the going got tough.

Module #22
The First Cornerstone of Perseverance is Preparation

"Genius and success are one percent inspiration and ninety-nine percent perspiration."

THOMAS EDISON

Our goal for this module

To appreciate how preparing for potential obstacles and setbacks in advance makes it easier to plow through when they arise.

No sports team ever won a game because of the pregame pep rally—no matter how attractive the cheerleaders are, no matter how loudly they cheer. Teams win games because they are prepared— physically, intellectually, and emotionally.

Bad things will happen—even to you

It is a sad truth that bad things do happen to good people. Money troubles, career crashes, health problems, family issues—sooner or later you're likely to experience them all. Although you cannot know the specific nature and/or timing of each future adverse event, you can still generally prepare yourself to deal with them more effectively. Just as the fire department trains in general in order to be prepared for the unknowable specific, you can and should prepare yourself at multiple levels to be ready for whatever might come along in your world. More than that, you can prepare yourself to not allow those bad things to make a victim out of you by the way in which you deal with them.

The first step is developing good habits and discipline

One of the most important steps toward preparing for what the future might bring is to prepare yourself—to build strong character by internalizing and operationalizing *The Twelve Core Action Values*, to get the education and develop the skills that will be required for you to achieve your goals, and to develop the habits that will keep you moving confidently forward in the direction of your goals, no matter what the world throws at you. You've heard that overnight success takes ten (or maybe fifteen or twenty) years. That's a pretty long night! I can tell you this—it was not a night spent only on idle dreaming. Successful people conscientiously work to develop the habits and the character necessary for achieving their goals. Here's what basketball coach Rick Pitino had to say in his book *Success is a Choice*:

> *Good habits... are a safeguard against underachieving. They prevent laziness. They prevent floundering. They prevent listlessness. Good habits create organization and discipline in our lives. It's virtually impossible to achieve success without having good habits, virtually impossible to reach your full potential. And in times of stress, when you are being severely tested, good habits become even more important. They become the rock, the standard of behavior that we must stick with so that we don't get off track.*

Prepare yourself physically, intellectually, emotionally, and spiritually for the inevitable difficulties that lie ahead

Think of the last time the roof fell in on your world, or the bottom dropped out from under it. It was exhausting, wasn't it? Depending upon the nature of the setback, you might have been wiped out physically, intellectually, emotionally, even spiritually. Mention problems like the death of a loved one, bankruptcy, a child in trouble, the loss of a job—and watch nods of agreement as people think about being knocked flat by such occurrences. Knowing that sooner or later bad things will happen, it makes sense to prepare now, doesn't it? And to prepare at four levels—physically, intellectually, emotionally, and spiritually.

Physical condition

If you are in shape physically, you're more likely to fight off anxiety and depression, and to have the energy you need to cope with a tough situation creatively and effectively.

Intellectual knowledge

If you are prepared intellectually, you will have more creative ideas and a higher level of confidence for dealing with any situation. For example, at some point or another, everybody has money troubles. You can prepare now by working to stay on top of your finances, reading good books on financial management, and finding out how other people have dealt with the types of problems you might anticipate someday having yourself.

Emotional strength

Times of adversity and difficulty are emotionally draining, and even more so if emotions flare out of control (for example, temper tantrums, panic attacks, or deep blue funks). One of the best ways of preparing for this is anticipating the types of problems you are likely to face, the emotional reactions they are likely to provoke, and then programming yourself with some sort of early warning system to prevent victim thinking and self-sabotaging behavior in response.

Spiritual peace

Prepare yourself spiritually for life's sucker punches by reaffirming your nurturing beliefs and questioning beliefs that are harmful. For many people, a regular habit of praying to be given the strength if (or when) disaster strikes is a helpful way of preparing to persevere through it.

Prepare for the worst, expect the best

Since we often tend to get what we expect out of life, it is important to remember that even as you prepare for the worst, you should expect the best.

Think about the worst thing that could happen in the year to come. How can you prepare yourself for the eventuality—physically, emotionally, intellectually, and spiritually? Now think about the best possible outcome if that adverse event were actually to occur—the *expect a miracle* outcome? What can you do now to transform apparent adversity into a miraculous outcome?

Avoid analysis paralysis

Preparation can become an end in itself, and we end up in a ready-aim-aim-aim-aim mode. Tom Peters was co-author (along with Bob Waterman) the best-selling business book *In Search of Excellence*. Today, Peters says that only one of the eight criteria that they used to define excellence has stood the test of time—a bias for action. There is a time, in other words, when you need to stop preparing and to start doing.

Rules for the Journey

1) Prepare for the worst, expect the best.

2) Take care of yourself physically by getting enough sleep, keeping yourself hydrated and eating a balanced diet, and making time for regular exercise so that when adversity strikes, you have the stamina to cope with it.

3) Conscientiously develops the habits and the character that are necessary for achieving your goals,

4) Avoid analysis paralysis; at some point you need to stop preparing and start acting.

5) Your trajectory is more important than your current position. It follows directly that if you want to be better off in the future, you must change your trajectory today. Very often, you can do this immediately and dramatically simply by changing your frame of mind.

Take-home exercise: Set 10-4-5 goals for yourself

I am a big believer in the power of what I call 10-4-5 goals. Whatever change you're trying to make, if you can achieve a *10 percent* improvement *for* each of the next *5 years*, you will make awesome progress. Increase your savings by ten percent every year for five years, increase the amount of time you devote to exercise by ten percent for each of the next five years, increase the number of worthwhile books you read by ten percent for each of the next five years. It's a power play on the old saw that "inch-by-inch, it's a cinch."

Extra credit reading

"Let me suggest that the bad things that happen to us in our lives do not have a meaning when they happen to us. They do not happen for any good reason which would cause us to accept them willingly. But we can give them a meaning. We can redeem these tragedies from senselessness by imposing meaning on them. The question we should be asking is not, 'Why did this happen to me? What did I do to deserve this?' That is really an unanswerable, pointless question. A better question would be 'Now that this has happened to me, what am I going to do about it?'"

HAROLD KUSHNER: *When Bad Things Happen to Good People*

Something to think about

Napoleon Hill, author of the classic self-help book *Think and Grow Rich*, wrote that every successful person finds that their greatest accomplishments occur just after they have become convinced that their ideas will not work, but kept at it anyway. Apparent failure is nothing more than a dress rehearsal for future success.

Module #23
The Second Cornerstone of Perseverance is Perspective

"Success is the ability to bounce from one failure to another without loss of enthusiasm."

WINSTON CHURCHILL

Our goal for this module

To realize that it is within our power to view any situation with a positive perspective, and to seek the blessings and opportunities—however well hidden they might be—within adversity.

My brother and his wife raised their triplets in London, where they attended British schools. When the children were twelve years old, the family moved back to the States. To prepare, my brother quizzed the kids on American history. One day, he asked one of the girls if she knew the significance of the year 1776. *"Yes, Daddy,"* she replied, *"that was the year King George lost the colonies."* Did Americans gain independence or did King George lose the colonies? Is it the best of times or the worst of times? Where you stand depends upon where you sit. Where you sit is determined upon your choice of a seat. Make sure you pick a good one!

Choose a positive perspective

One of the most important choices we all make every day–in fact, every minute of every day—is how we see ourselves, other people, and events in the world around us. It is much easier to persevere through the inevitable obstacles and setbacks that life will throw your way if you consciously strive to maintain a positive perspective.

Oh, yeah, this is the part where...

You might have heard that one of the best ways to be successful yourself is to study how other successful people have already accomplished whatever it is that you desire to accomplish. Good advice, indeed. But while you're at it, also study their setbacks and failures, and the crises they had to overcome en route to victory. Then, if and when those things befall you, remind yourself:

> *Oh, yeah—this is the part of the drama where our hero falls off his horse right at the feet of the fire-breathing dragon and all appears to be lost, but he finds a way to hang on one more minute and gloriously snatches victory from the jaws of defeat.*

As Joseph Campbell said in his book *The Power of Myth*: *"One of the things that comes out in myths... is that at the bottom of the abyss comes the voice of salvation. The black moment when the real message of transformation is going to come. At the darkest moment comes the light."*

Problems and predicaments

It's useful to distinguish between problems and predicaments. A problem can be solved; a predicament must be lived with. An alcoholic neighbor is a problem; an alcoholic mother-in-law is a predicament. When Reinhold Niebuhr wrote the Serenity Prayer, he was really asking for the wisdom to distinguish between problems (the courage to change what can be changed) and predicaments (the serenity to accept what cannot be changed). One of the most frustrating experiences in the world is dealing with a predicament as though it was a problem. Sometimes, the first step to maintaining a positive perspective is simply figuring out whether you've got a problem or predicament on your hands. Think about the most serious and/or frustrating challenges facing you right now. Are they problems or are they predicaments? If they're problems, what action can you take—starting right now—to deal with them? And if they're predicaments, remind yourself to accept them with equanimity, since there's nothing you can do about them anyway.

> *"God, grant me the serenity to accept the things I cannot change, the courage to change the things I can, and the wisdom to know the difference."*
>
> *REINHOLD NIEBUHR:* **The Serenity Prayer**

The power of hope

Whether the test you are facing is in school, at work, or in life, make hope your secret weapon. Research by Dr. Martin Seligman, author of *Learned Optimism,* shows that hope—the expectation of success—is the single-best predictor of actual success. So stand unconquered for one more day, prepare yourself for each successive test you know will be coming, and fire up your hope.

THE HOPE DIAMOND

The most precious diamond in the world cannot be purchased, it can only be accepted.

The most precious diamond in the world cannot be seen, it can only be felt.

The most precious diamond in the world cannot be worn around your neck, it can only be kept safe in your heart.

The most precious diamond in the world cannot be taken away, it can only be given away.

The most precious diamond in the world is free for the asking, and you can have as many as you ask for.

The most precious diamond in the world is stronger than iron, but is more fragile than a dream.

The most precious diamond in the world is always genuine, because there is no such thing as false hope.

From The Healing Tree, by Joe Tye

Reach out to help someone with a bigger problem

One of the best ways to maintain a positive perspective on your problems is to help someone who has an even bigger problem. This is a guiding principle of Alcoholics Anonymous, known as "mutuality," a term that reflects the fact that one person cannot help another without both of them benefiting in some way. The best way, and in many cases the only way, the recovering alcoholic can remain sober is through a commitment to helping other people gain and retain sobriety. Making a human connection by reaching out to help someone else can give a sense of meaning to an otherwise meaningless tragedy.

Thank God Ahead of Time

Thank God Ahead of Time is the title of a book by Michael Crosby, but it is also a great philosophy for life. Even the most tragic adversity usually brings some benefit in its wake (think about what people say two years after having lost a job; it's almost always: *"best thing that ever could have happened!"*). This can apply to something even as devastating as a diagnosis of cancer. While nobody is glad to have the disease, many people have found strength and grace through the trial. Essentially, it boils down to the choice of being a victim, or accepting the circumstance and then creating meaning in what otherwise might just be a meaningless tragedy.

 ## Rules for the Journey

1) Best of times or worst of times? It's your choice, and the more disciplined you are at discerning the best of every situation, the more often you will obtain the best of outcomes.

2) The glass is neither half-empty not half-full; it's completely full. Half with the water you need to drink and half with the air you need to breathe. There are blessings everywhere if you pay attention for them.

3) Another name for perseverance could be the ability to tolerate frustration, to not allow frustration to deter you from pursuing your goals, whatever they are. In fact, if you're not routinely being frustrated, then either your goals are too small or you're not trying very hard to achieve them, or both.

4) Life is a motion picture, not a snapshot, and your trajectory is more important than where you are at any point in time. There's opportunity hidden in every adversity if you have the strength and courage to search for it and to pursue it when you've found it.

5) Any time one person helps another, two people are helped. Whenever you find yourself anxious, depressed, or frustrated, go out of your way to help someone else who is anxious, depressed and frustrated. Whatever you most need in life, the best way for you to get it is to help someone else who needs it even more than you do.

 ## Take-home exercise: TGAoT—Thank God Ahead of Time

Think about the adversity you most dread. Perhaps its losing your job, or losing your health. You might also be focused on a bigger picture, concerned about poverty and homelessness, or the environmental impact of global warming. Think about how you might find a source of gratitude, or at least create some semblance of meaning, should any of the dreaded adversities actually occur. Now, imagine the letters TGAoT (for Thank God Ahead of Time) tattooed on the inside of your forehead as a constant reminder to be grateful for, and not resentful of, the difficulties you encounter. In my experience, and in the experience of many people I've worked with, thinking *prospectively* about the TGAoT response to any adversity will make it far more likely that you will respond in a positive and empowered way, and not play the role of the victim.

 ### Extra credit reading

"The one common link among all unstoppable people is adversity—they struggled, tripped and stumbled, and had setbacks and failures, but they pulled themselves up and kept on going. The dream demanded their all and they gave it. The challenges and hardships they faced seemed insurmountable and yet they surmounted them. With each trial, they emerged stronger, surer, and more deserving of the dream itself."

CYNTHIA KERSEY: *Unstoppable: 45 Powerful Stories of Perseverance and Triumph from People Just Like You*

Something to think about

Don't confuse verbs and adjectives with nouns. Losing a job (verb) or being a losing candidate (adjective) does not make you a loser (noun).

Module #24
The Third Cornerstone of Perseverance is Toughness

"Keep on beginning and failing. Each time you fail, start all over again, and you will grow stronger until you have accomplished a purpose—not the one you began with perhaps, but one you'll be glad to remember."

ANNE SULLIVAN

Our goal for this module

To internalize the need for, and the power of, mental and emotional toughness for surmounting adversity, and for turning apparent dead-ends into doors opening onto opportunity and success.

When it feels like you're deep in the valley of the shadow of death, you might not feel particularly courageous as you claw your way through, one day at a time. You might not feel the strength of character you're gaining through your trials during those times of trial. It's only later, after you've emerged from the valley and can look back down from the sunlit heights above that you can appreciate the transformation that has occurred in you. You must walk through the valley on faith, one step at a time, that you will climb out into the sunshine and the fresh air above.

The difference between winners and also-rans

Quite often the main difference between winners and also-rans is simply that winners refuse to quit, even when to all outside appearances the battle has been lost. Nearly 2,500 years ago, Wu Ch'i wrote in his tract on the art of war that on the battlefield, those who are determined to die with glory will live, while those who merely hope to escape with their lives will die. In today's world, the person who is determined to carve his or her own path and to achieve magnificent goals will live a rewarding and fulfilling life, while the one whose life is dominated by fears of rejection and failure, and whose greatest hope is simply making it to retirement, will suffer endless emotional stress.

Don't whine, make excuses, blame others, or be a victim

John Wooden, the legendary UCLA college basketball coach, said that you will inevitably lose games, but you're never a loser until you start blaming somebody else for your loss. Whenever you complain, make excuses, blame other people, or otherwise act like a victim you are saying to the world, and to yourself, that there's nothing you can do to deal with your predicament. It's what psychologists call "learned helplessness." Any time you find yourself operating in this mode, go back and re-read the Seven Simple Promises of *The Self Empowerment Pledge*.

Be tough on your inner critic

When I was an MBA student at the Stanford Graduate School of Business, one of the most rewarding classes I took was Creativity in Business, taught by Michael Ray. We learned that one of the most serious impediments to creativity and innovation happens to be our own inner critic—what Professor Ray called the Voice Of Judgment. More often than we recognize, VOJ underlies all of our fears—fear of rejection, of failure, of commitment, of success. Sometimes you can reason with VOJ, or seduce it into silence. At other times, however, it simply must be beaten into submission. Stand up to that negative, judgmental little inner voice, talk back to it, and if necessary, give it a good old-fashioned punch in the nose.

> *"Keep your spirits up, don't allow yourself to be depressed, and never for one moment doubt but that matters will finish better and more quickly than you imagine."*
>
> NAPOLEON BONAPARTE

Transform despair into determination

When Ernest Shackleton's ship *Endurance* was first trapped in and then crushed by Antarctic ice in 1916, one of his most daunting challenges was to maintain the morale of his twenty-eight crew members during their 634-day ordeal. In *Leading at the Edge*, leadership consultant Dennis N.T. Perkins and his co-authors describe some of the strategies that Shackleton used to hold his team together and bring them all home alive:

Keep moving

Shackleton kept his men busy, knowing that idleness can foster a sense of lost control, which in turn leads to despair.

Don't berate, celebrate

Shackleton was quick to defuse conflict, and used every excuse to hold a party or celebration of some sort.

Nurture hope with constructive action

Shackleton made sure his men understood that he had no doubt whatsoever they would all survive, and set a personal example of courage and self-sacrifice in doing the things that were necessary for that to occur.

Innovate your way around brick walls

Shackleton encouraged creative thinking to solve what appeared to be intractable problems, and when inaction would have been a fatal choice, he was willing to take what otherwise would have seemed unthinkable risks.

Shackleton knew that a leader's first duty during tough times is to maintain hope and optimism, and to stave off despair, no matter how desperate the situation might seem. In retrospect, one can speculate on how frequently members of the crew were tempted to quit before the breakthrough that led to their rescue. He later wrote: *"I have marveled often at the thin line that divides success from failure and the sudden turn that leads from apparently certain disaster to comparative safety."*

You never "can't"

Any time you catch yourself uttering those toxic two words, *"I can't,"* remind yourself that it's probably not true. What you're really saying is that you don't want to, that it would be difficult or expensive, or that there are other things that you would rather do.

Be today, see tomorrow

One of the greatest challenges of perseverance is keeping a tight reign on both awareness and imagination during times of difficulty. *Awareness* is of the present; *imagination* is of the future. This is the time dimension to perspective. I call it the *Be Today, See Tomorrow* principle: keep your *attention* in the present, keep your *vision* in the future, and know when to give priority to each: when your perspective should be in the right-here-and-now, and when it should be in the better-days-to-come.

> *When afraid for tomorrow*
>
> *concentrate your attention*
>
> *on the work of today*
>
> *When afraid for today*
>
> *fix your vision*
>
> *on the dreams of tomorrow*
>
> MCZEN

Don't quit before you even start

Sometimes we quit before we even start by giving in to our doubts and fears, by procrastinating until the opportunity has passed, by not even trying. People usually quit *emotionally* before they quit physically. For example, most business failures, once you scrape away the standard excuses of inadequate cash flow, excessive government regulation, unfair competition, inadequate employees and the like, are ultimately emotional failures—loss of courage, faith, or energy, or all three at once. What you can do to prevent such an emotional collapse from derailing you in the march toward your dreams and goals?

A tough love message

Low self-esteem (buying into those negative labels) is more often than not just an excuse for laziness and cowardice. If you really believe that the members of a group don't like you, and suspect that it's because you don't deserve to be liked, you won't make much of an effort to become part of the group. If you really believe that you're not capable of making something happen, you probably won't find the courage to try. In either case, you end up creating a self-fulfilling prophecy. That's why I believe that we all have an absolute obligation to challenge self-limiting labels and enhance our own self-image and self-esteem—so that we will have the courage and the energy to make a difference.

Get the help you need, including counseling if necessary

Toughness does not mean going it on your own, Lone Ranger style. Sometimes it requires mental toughness to admit to yourself that you need help, including possible professional counseling (which in some cases may also include therapy and/ or medication) to get you back on an even keel so you can think clearly and pursue your goals. It is a sign of strength, not of weakness, to ask for help.

 ## Rules for the Journey

1) Be tough on yourself by having high standards and expectations, but do not be tough on yourself by beating yourself up if you do not always live up to those standards and expectations.

2) Get into the habit of doing the difficult things first. Being tough with yourself means doing what you *should* do before you do what you *want* to do. It means tackling the unpleasant little problems before they have the chance to grow into big problems.

3) Any project or initiative can look like failure in the middle, but it only becomes a failure when you quit striving.

4) One of the most important things you can do to increase your mental and emotional toughness is change the way you talk to yourself. Most negative self-talk is false and self-sabotaging; so rewrite those scripts.

5) Positive enthusiasm and mental toughness are hardest to find at precisely those times where they are most important, which is why it's essential to cultivate the underlying strength of character before it's required.

6) Complacence and despair—both are mortal enemies of success. Complacence can seduce you to stop fighting before the battle is truly won; despair can induce you to stop fighting before the battle is truly lost.

 ### Take-home exercise: Gain future strength by learning from past adversity

Think back on the most severe setbacks you have suffered in your life. For each one, write about how you felt at the time of the crisis—the emotions you were feeling, and what you perceived as your prospects for the future. Then, looking back on that time from the perspective to today, contemplate some of the ways that you are stronger personally, and are in a better position in terms of your current circumstances, than would have been the case had it never happened. Now think about what these observations have to say about any adversity you might currently be enduring, or might have to face in the days to come.

Important Reminder

The 23rd Psalm says that we pass through the valley of the shadow of death, not that we take up permanent residence down there in the shadows!

 ### Extra credit reading

"Courage is the heart to keep trying, even when one has tasted bitter failure... The more determined we are to fight our troubles tooth and nail, the more likely we are to triumph over them."

JOHN CARMODY: *How to Handle Trouble: A Guide to Peace of Mind*

Something to think about

Samurai Paradox: When your body is strong, it will bend to your commands, but when it is weak, you must give in to its demands.

Module #25
The Fourth Cornerstone of Perseverance is Learning

"If only it were possible for us to see farther than our knowledge reaches, and even a little beyond the outworks of our presentiment, perhaps we would bear our sadness with greater trust than we have in our joys."

RAINER MARIA RILKE

Our goal for this module

To see adversity as the opportunity to learn from our mistakes and failures, and emerge from the experiences stronger and wiser and ready to try again.

During the dot-com boom of the 1990s, lots of young internet millionaires believed they'd reinvented the way the business world works. It didn't matter if you weren't making any money, they said, all that mattered were things like website hits and eyeball stickiness. They were, of course, quite wrong. Many of their companies crashed and burned in the great internet bust. After their fancy offices were repossessed and the fire sales on their deluxe office furniture were over, the smart ones went back home and started new business ventures working out of their garages. As is always the case, they learned far more important lessons from their failures than they did from their successes.

Learning is the fruit of adversity

Nobody in their right mind consciously seeks out adversity, and very few of us welcome it when it arrives. It is a fact of life, however, that some amount of adversity is necessary for your growth and learning. King Solomon began the book of Proverbs by stating that a wise person will hear and increase learning, and that a person of understanding will seek wise counsel. At about the same time, but on the other side of the earth, Lao Tzu said that one who knows others is wise, while one who knows oneself is enlightened. Self-awareness is a continuous, life-long process of learning and introspection, and times of adversity tend to be where the best of that learning and introspection occurs.

The four benefits of adversity

Nobody looks forward to having bad things happen, but whether we want it or not, bad things will happen. It is then our choice whether or not to derive the benefits that often come in the wake of adversity. Here are four good things that can happen when bad things happen:

Benefit #1: Times of difficulty are essential to build character

Adversity is like the physical therapist in a burn unit: in an already painful situation, it causes even more pain, but if you can endure that pain you will emerge stronger and more flexible. That which doesn't kill you will make you stronger, but only if you plumb the experience for it's lessons.

Benefit #2: We learn more from failure than we do from success

In their book *Built to Last*, Jim Collins and Jerry Porras found that many of the most successful corporations had to overcome serious setbacks in their early years. The lessons they describe are as applicable to you personally and professionally as they are to the large corporations studied in that book, including this one: *"Since you can't tell ahead of time which variations will prove to be favorable, you have to accept mistakes and failures as an integral part of the evolutionary process."*

"Use your mistakes as a springboard into new areas of discovery; accidents can hold the key to innovation. When things fall apart, make art. Carry this spirit through to every area of your life."

PHILIP TOSHIO SUDO: *Zen Guitar*

Benefit #3: Adversity can open doors and identify opportunities

One door closes, another door opens, goes the old proverb. It is often in the face of seeming adversity that the greatest opportunities open before us. Many a fired or laid off worker has started a business they never otherwise would have begun, and gone on to become highly successful. Some of the most effective and compassionate counselors and caregivers are those who through their own adversity opened the door to helping others.

Benefit #4: Times of adversity are often when we meet the people who end up being most important in our lives

Anyone who has ever participated in a support group of any kind has seen this phenomenon: people come to their first meeting shattered, despondent, and convinced that they will never be whole again. A while later, they are filled with hope and courage, and have made many new friends. And in time, it is their turn to help others find a sense of meaning in what otherwise could be a meaningless tragedy.

Train your doubt

Train your doubt. That was the advice given by the German poet Rilke in his *Letters to a Young Poet*. Don't let doubt torment you, and don't let it paralyze you, but also don't ignore it. Rather, teach it to ask questions that will resolve your skepticism. When the voice of doubt says, *"it will never work,"* force it to answer questions like, *"what needs to be changed so that it will work?"* Having your doubt work for you and not against you is a key element of perseverance.

Ask great questions during times of adversity

Adversity often presents a fork in the road; taking the correct turn can depend upon asking the correct questions. After losing a job, for example, questions such as *"why me"* or *"how will I make ends meet"* tend to create a pessimistic victim mindset. On the other hand, questions like *"should I go back to school?"* or *"how can I raise the money to start my own business?"* can lead to answers that will position you to be in a very different, and better, place at some point down the road.

Asking intelligent (and courageous) questions is often more important than receiving technically correct answers. Here are some examples:

What is this adversity trying to teach me about myself?

What must happen so that two (or five or ten) years from now I look back and say to myself that this was the best thing that ever could have happened?

What patterns in my attitudes and behaviors tend to contribute to repeating problems (debt, job loss, failed relationships) and what can I do to change those patterns?

Who am I meant to connect with, or to build a stronger relationship with, through the process of dealing with this apparent adversity?

Who else has experienced a similar setback, how did they deal with it, and what can I learn from their experience?

Get frustrated – constructively

You've worked all week on your sales pitch, but two minutes into the presentation it's already clear that they're not even listening. *Frustration!* You go into your annual performance review expecting praise and a raise, but instead you're given a pink slip and your last check. *Frustration!* You've just finished proofreading your first short story, and it's terrible. *Frustration!* Another name for perseverance could be the ability to tolerate frustration, to not allow frustration to deter you from pursuing your goals, whatever they are. If you're not routinely being frustrated, then either your goals are too small or you're not trying very hard to achieve them, or both. The ability to not only confront frustration, but to catalyze it into the energy for revitalized intentionality, is one of the master skills of success. As Anthony Robbins said in his book *Unlimited Power*: *"The key to success is massive frustration. Look at almost any great success, and you'll find there's been massive frustration along the way...There are two kinds of people—those who've handled frustration and those who wish they had."*

See yourself as a coach and a teacher

As a leader (and we are all leaders in some situations), you should play a role analogous to the manager in a boxer's corner during a prize fight. If your "fighter" has taken a pounding in the round just ended, he doesn't need you hovering over his stool at the break telling him what an idiot he is, which is the approach all too many managers take in dealing with subordinate failure in their organizations. A good manager does two things in the brief time he has before the fight resumes. First, he gives the fighter technical advice on how to avoid getting beat up again, and hopefully to turn the tables on his opponent. Second, he gives his man the confidence that he can do it.

Never Quit does not mean don't stop

When I'm speaking about *Never Fear, Never Quit,* I distinguish between stopping and quitting. If something isn't working and likely is not going to work, the best thing is to stop and try something else. For the person who feels burned out on the job and dreads even getting out of bed in the morning, the smartest thing might well be to stop—to find another line of work that can be performed with greater enthusiasm and a sense of meaning, even if it entails a temporary financial or status setback. Quitting, on the other hand, is giving up emotionally, giving in to the paralysis of anxiety and despair. Paradoxically, a failure to *stop* before excessive losses pile up can increase the likelihood that a catastrophic emotional melt-down will cause you to *quit.* Sometimes you have to stop following the original plan and redirect your efforts in order to optimize hopes for success in achieving your ultimate goal.

 ## Rules for the Journey

1) That which doesn't kill you will make you stronger, but only if you plumb the experience for it's lessons. Times of difficulty build strong character.

2) We learn and grow more from our setbacks than we do from our successes. Adversity prepares you for bigger challenges and accomplishments in the future.

3) One door closes, another door opens, goes the old proverb. It's often in the face of seeming adversity that the greatest opportunities open before us. When things aren't working, it forces you to seek more creative solutions.

4) Adversity connects us with other people in ways that are more meaningful than the connections that come through playing and working together.

5) Adversity keeps on teaching; your setbacks can, if you're committed to learning from them, also be the source of great learning for others.

 ## Take-home exercise: Open a book to a random page

Here's a great idea for enhancing your learning: go to your bookshelf, or into a library or bookstore, find the self-help section, randomly select a book from the shelves, then open that book to a random page and start reading. Chances are good that very quickly, you will find a bit of advice that, if you follow it, will improve the quality of the outcomes that you are achieving in your life. As I was working on this particular module, I tried it myself. My mind was wandering and I was about to decide that I should knock off for the day. But first, I walked over to my bookshelf and pulled out a book, opened it to a random page, and read the passage that is included below. It just so happened that this was the advice I most needed to follow at that particular moment, and that what I really needed to do was get back to work and finish my work.

Extra credit reading

"I don't think most people realize how stressful it can be to have multiple incomplete tasks hanging over your head... It has always intrigued me because often, it would be relatively easy and simple to bear down and complete something—not almost complete something, but really complete it 100 percent and get it out of the way... This is an easy habit to break. Take an honest look at your own tendencies. If you are someone who often almost finishes something, take note of the tendency and commit yourself to that last final completion. You can do it—and when you do, your life is going to seem so much easier."

RICHARD CARLSON: *Don't Sweat the Small Stuff at Work*

Something to think about

The 23ʳᵈ Psalm says that we pass through the valley of the shadow of death, not that we take up permanent residence!

Geologists tell us that about one million years ago there was a lava dam on the Colorado River that created a lake which dwarfed the lakes created by the Hoover and Glen Canyon dams put together. Today all that remains of that dam are chunks of black lava seen downriver from Lava Falls in the Grand Canyon. It's a great metaphor—no matter how big the barriers appear to be, relentless pressure will eventually break through.

Core Action Value #6 is Faith

Throughout history, faith has been a powerful source of strength and solace for humans, a power that transcends specific religious beliefs and practices (or their absence). Faith only begins at the point where certainty ends.

Cornerstone #1: Gratitude

Complaining is the anti-prayer—whining about blessings that have not (yet) showed up rather than being thankful for those that have.

Cornerstone #2: Forgiveness

The real beneficiary of forgiveness is not the one who is being forgiven, it's the one who is doing the forgiving.

Cornerstone #3: Love

The Beatles were right: there's nothing you can do that can't be done and there's no one you can save that can't be saved—all you need is love.

Cornerstone #4: Spirituality

People who really do believe that whoever dies with the most toys wins end up being the biggest losers in life.

"People don't want more information. They are up to their eyeballs in information. They want faith—faith in you, your goals, your success, in a story you tell. It is faith that moves mountains, not facts. Facts do not give birth to faith. Faith needs a story to sustain it—a meaningful story that inspires belief in you and renews hope that your ideas indeed offer what you promise."

ANNETTE SIMMONS: *The Story Factor: Inspiration, Influence, and Persuasion through the Art of Storytelling*

Module #26
Core Action Value #6 is Faith

"Pursue some path, however narrow and crooked, in which you can walk with love and reverence."

HENRY DAVID THOREAU

Our goal for this module

To distinguish faith from religion, and to explore some of the ways that each of us can strengthen our own faith and apply that power in our lives.

In the truest and original sense of the word, to have faith does not mean that you accept without question a certain religious dogma. Rather, it means that you act with fidelity (as in being faithful to another person or to a cause), and that you have trust in something that is beyond your own power to control (as in trusting in God, or trusting in the future, during times of difficulty). Is there any community, any organization, or any family that could not be strengthened by such faith?

The power of faith

From the beginning of recorded history, faith has been the most powerful source of human motivation. People have exerted themselves and taken risks for the sake of faith that never would have been motivated in a quest for material gain or personal power. In *The Corporate Mystic*, Gay Hendricks and Kate Ludeman predict that in the years to come, the most effective *business* leadership will be first and foremost *spiritual* leadership. They go on to say that leaders who think that spirituality has no place in the world of business are selling themselves, their people, and their organizations short.

Ours has been called the age of anxiety, in no small part because of the rapid pace of change and the uncertainty which that creates. Remember the Serenity Prayer:

"God grant me the courage to change what I can, the serenity to accept what I cannot, and the wisdom to know the difference." For many people, the source of serenity is faith. We might not be able to reduce the pace of change or eliminate the uncertainty, but one thing we can do is honor people's individual faith, and provide an environment that strengthens it.

The loving wisdom of Mother Teresa

In her book *A Simple Path* Mother Teresa said that we are all children of the same God, and thus she saw her job as helping people grow stronger in their own faiths, not converting them to hers. How could helping others grow in their faith, rather than trying to convert them to your beliefs, help *you* grow stronger in *your* faith?

Real faith is reflected in loving acceptance of others

For thousands of years, religious intolerance has been (and continues to be) the cause of, or the excuse for, heartbreaking hatred and violence. Even Hitler's death camp guards wore belt buckles inscribed with the words, *"God with us."* There is much that is beautiful, loving, and generous in the Bible, and in the three religions that look to it for truth. There are, however, some parts of the Bible—in both testaments—which, if taken literally, portray a God who is petty, vicious, vindictive, and violent—and who commands us to be likewise (for example, instructing us to give our slaves the day off on the Sabbath—it's right there in *The Ten Commandments*).

Unfortunately, too many people do take those parts literally. As theological scholar Elaine Pagels writes in her book Beyond Belief, many Christians *"tend to assume that only one side can speak the truth, while others speak only lies—or evil. Many still insist that only their church... or only the group within their church with which they agree—actually remains faithful to Jesus' teaching."* This narrowness, this tendency to equate being different with being wrong, or with being evil, diminishes our churches and it diminishes us as human beings. Worse, it diminishes God, transforming the divine into a caricature of our own fears, prejudices, and hatreds.

"You can safely assume that you've created God in your own image when it turns out that God hates all the people you do."

ANN LAMOTT: *Bird by Bird*

Think hard about your beliefs

Have you have read *The True Believer* by Eric Hoffer? It is a deeply disturbing book. The "faith" of Hoffer's true believer is not faith at all, it's fanatic attachment to dogma, unshakable by logic or facts and absolutely intolerant of questions and doubt. Real faith, on the other hand, struggles with the most difficult of questions, including those presented in scripture. Is wealth and good fortune the sign of God's pleasure, or is it harder for a rich man to get to heaven than a camel to pass through the eye of a needle? Should we pray for the sword of God to be with us when we attack our enemies, or should we turn the other cheek at their offenses? Is God the vengeful judge or the merciful redeemer? I do not know the answers to these questions. Neither do you. Nobody does. But I do know this: thinking critically about such questions is more likely to strengthen your faith than it is to weaken it. On the other hand, to blindly accept nonsense because "it's right there in the Bible" is not the way of true faith—it's the way of the true believer.

 ## Rules for the Journey

1) Build your own inner strength and peace upon the four pillars of faith: faith in yourself, faith in other people, faith in the future, and faith in a higher power that is much bigger than the physical world (what I and many others call God).

2) Let your faith and your gratitude for all that you have been blessed with shine through in your attitudes and in your actions (Sunday's Promise of *The Self-Empowerment Pledge*).

3) True faith is strengthened and tempered in the cauldron of doubt; do not shut the door in the face of difficult questions, but rather let them in, explore their meaning, and let them lead you to deeper answers than can be yielded by merely parroting the liturgy.

4) Faith is bigger and deeper than belief; beliefs can, will and should change as one grows and learns, but faith endures.

 ## Take-home exercise: Think about your faith and your beliefs

Make a list of some of your most important religious beliefs. If it were somehow proved beyond the shadow of a doubt that they were all incorrect (e.g., that Jonah really did not spend three days in the belly of a fish deep in the ocean and live to tell about it), would it shatter your faith? Or would you find a way to transcend errant factual beliefs and instead inspire even stronger faith? Here are four questions to think about how your faith is reflected in your attitudes and in your behaviors:

Question 1: What are the blessings you are grateful for, and what (or what more) can (or should) you do to express your gratitude?

Question 2: Who do you need to forgive, and for what (beginning with yourself)?

Question 3: Within your own small sphere of influence, what can you do to foster a more loving world?

Question 4: How can you, for even a few minutes each day, escape the clutches of our materialistic, entertainment-obsessed world and experience the true joy of the spirit unbound by such superficial trappings?

Extra credit reading

"God is the divided original whose divided image we remain. He is the restless breathing we still hear in our sleep."

JACK MILES: *God: A Biography*

Something to think about

The pot of gold is an illusion; only the rainbow is real.

Module #27
The First Cornerstone of Faith
is Gratitude

"I want to go on living even after my death! And therefore I am grateful to God for giving me this gift, this possibility of declaring myself and of writing, of expressing all that is in me. I can shake off everything if I write; my sorrows disappear, my courage is reborn."

ANNE FRANK

Our goal for this module

To encourage you to think about the things that really matter, and to reflect upon all of the things for which you are (or should be) grateful, and to understand gratitude as one of the pillars of living faith (regardless of particular religious beliefs).

What does the Lord's Prayer say about tomorrow's bread? That's right—nothing. *"Give us this day our daily bread."* The message is to be thankful for the blessings of your life, and to not be resentful about blessings that you do not (yet) have in your life. As the great philosopher William James put it over one hundred years ago, the more concerned somebody is with material acquisition, the less free their lives will be. So in that sense, gratitude is the key to freedom.

Gratitude is the foundation of faith

Gratitude is a central tenet of faith in most of the world's spiritual traditions. People make sacrifices, they fast, they meditate, and they pray in part to express their gratitude for the blessings (past, present, and future) of their lives. Especially those of us living in the developed world today have a great deal to be thankful for. We are blessed in so many ways: unprecedented life expectancy, medical technology that is nothing short of miraculous, and living standards beyond the wildest dreams of people who lived in our world as recently as the Great Depression. But you wouldn't know it, listening to the way people complain and moan about every little thing.

Gratitude is more than just saying thank you. It is *choosing* to see best of times, even in the worst of times. It is *choosing* to keep your mouth shut when it feels right and just to complain. It is *choosing* to walk away from a pickle-sucker rather than encourage their BMW (bitching, moaning, and whining) with commiseration (co-miserate: to be miserable together). It is *choosing* to share when the natural inclination is to hoard. In short, genuine gratitude is hard emotional work. And it is demanded of us, who have been given so much.

> *Complaining is the un-prayer. Instead of expressing your gratitude for the blessings of your life, you are expressing your resentment for what you don't (yet) have. You cannot simultaneously be grateful and resentful.*

Gratitude is the platform from which hope arises

When all else fails, there is always hope. No matter how bad things seem to be, you can always hope for the best. And unlike knowing or believing, you do not have to justify hope—you just hope. If you are grateful for what's right about your life, you are more likely to be hopeful for a brighter future than if you are bitter and resentful about what's wrong with your life. In this sense, an attitude of gratitude can actually help shape your future. Hope can bring about miracles.

In *Learned Optimism*, Dr. Seligman showed that optimistic people were more successful, more resilient, and healthier than pessimistic people, and that they were less prone to anxiety, depression, or physical illness. One of the most important differences between optimistic and pessimistic people, Seligman found, was in how they view the problems of their life. The pessimists tend to internalize their troubles, and view them as permanent, pervasive, and personal. Optimists, on the other hand, view their troubles as being temporary, specific, and external. And whereas optimists would routinely argue with their own negative self talk, and dispute self-blaming interpretations of failure or discouragement, pessimists tend to submissively accept the most self-limiting interpretations. The good news, Seligman shows with multiple scientific studies, is that somebody can learn how to be more optimistic and that in doing so they can change the results they achieve in life.

Things to *thank* about...

I'd rather spend a week hiking in the Grand Canyon than be in any Club Med or five star hotel anywhere in the world. One of the reasons I treasure my time in The Canyon is that it makes me appreciate the little blessings that are so easy to take for granted. Here's a small sampling:

Finding running water in what you thought would be a dry creek bed.

A shooting star etched out in a sky uncontaminated by ambient light.

The last handful of trail mix on the last day of a long solo.

A tent that doesn't leak in the rain.

A warm sleeping bag on a cold night.

A cold natural shower at Ribbon Falls.

A cold beer at Phantom Ranch.

Advil.

Beginning lifelong friendships with strangers met on the trail.

Hearing God whisper in your ear at the precise moment your ego has gotten bored by the lack of artificial entertainment and gone to sleep.

What are some of the things that you have to be thankful for?

Gratitude promotes health, happiness, and success

In the research project cited immediately below, Emmons and McCullough had three groups of people keep daily diaries. One group wrote about events of the day, the second group wrote about unpleasant experiences, and the third wrote only about things for which they were grateful. If you were to read the results of their study and substitute "magic pill" for "attitude of gratitude," you would assume massive advertising puffery. Their results were nothing short of astounding. You can be healthier and wealthier, happier and more at-peace. And it won't cost you a dime or require a visit to the pharmacy. All you need to do is replace greed and resentment with generosity and gratitude.

"Grateful people report higher levels of positive emotions, life satisfaction, vitality, optimism and lower levels of depression and stress. The disposition toward gratitude appears to enhance pleasant feeling states more than it diminishes unpleasant emotions."

ROBERT A. EMMONS AND MICHAEL E. MCCULLOUGH:
Research Project on Gratitude and Thankfulness

The gratitude of real faith is reflected in action

It's one of the oldest debates in Christianity: which prevails, faith or acts? The answer seems to be that genuine faith is always reflected in charitable acts, while engaging in "random acts of kindness" cannot help but to enhance faith. Genuine gratitude will be reflected in charity. It's more than just being thankful for what you have, it's wanting to share your blessings with others and to create blessings for those who are not as privileged as you happen to be.

"Walk into any Christian bookstore and you will see hundreds of books on what God can do for us. In fact, you will see one little book that advocates a blatantly selfish prayer that has become a runaway bestseller. But you will not find a single book on what Jesus warned we must do for others. Not one. Go ahead; try it and you will see I am not exaggerating."

JOHN SCOTT: "Decoding the Bible," in
Christian Ethics Today, December 2004

 ## Rules for the Journey

1) Gratitude is a central tenet of faith in most of the world's spiritual traditions. People make sacrifices, they fast, they meditate, and they pray in part to express their gratitude for the blessings (past, present, and future) of their lives.

2) Gratitude is more than just saying thank you. It is choosing to see best of times, even in the worst of times. It is choosing to be grateful when you feel more like complaining.

3) One of the great sources of anxiety in our society is the fear that we will not get what we want (or what we think we're entitled to), or that we will lose what we have. How can you, even for a few minutes each day, escape the clutches of our materialistic, entertainment-obsessed world and experience the true joy of the spirit unbound by such superficial trappings?

4) It's easy to fall into the trap of taking things for granted. Any time you find yourself feeling put upon by others, or feeling resentful for what you don't

have, remind yourself of all that others have done for you, and of all that you have been blessed with.

5) Be sure that your gratitude is reflected at work and at home by telling people how much you appreciate who they are and what they do.

 ## Take-home exercise: Be thankful in past, present, and future tense

Every morning upon waking and every evening at the end of the day, make a list of at least ten things for which you are grateful. Be especially alert for opportunities to transform the things about which you've been complaining ("my back is killing me") into a source of gratitude ("thank God for Advil!"). Then go one step further and be thankful for the blessings you haven't even realized yet. Get into the habit of "Thanking God Ahead of Time" for the as-of-yet unseen miracles that you would love to see happen in your life, as if they already had occurred. You will greatly increase the likelihood that they will occur.

 ## Extra credit reading

"Gratitude unlocks the fullness of life. It turns what we have into enough, and more. It turns denial into acceptance, chaos to order, confusion to clarity. It can turn a meal into a feast, a house into a home, a stranger into a friend. Gratitude makes sense of our past, brings peace for today, and creates a vision for tomorrow."

MELODY BEATTIE: *Codependent No More*

Something to think about

Gratitude is measured in minutes while resentment is measured in years.

Module #28
The Second Cornerstone of Faith is Forgiveness

"The weak can never forgive. Forgiveness is the attribute of the strong."

MOHANDAS GANDHI

Our goal for this module

To appreciate just how toxic and how damaging failure to forgive can be—physically, emotionally, and spiritually and to make the personal commitment to be a more forgiving person..

The *I Ching*, an ancient book of Chinese wisdom, reminds us that hatred is a chain that binds us to the object of our hatred. Forgiveness is the key that unlocks that chain, that frees us from the prison of our own venomous emotions.

The cure for emotional cancer

Carrying around a grudge is emotional cancer; it has been likened to drinking poison in hopes of killing someone else. The more you carry around anger, hatred, vengefulness, and other negative emotions from the past, the more difficult it will be to experience a strong sense of faith in your current world. Instead of living with gratitude and peace in the present, you are shackled to the dead weight of the past. Not only that, by hauling around vengeful emotions in the backpack of your life's journey, you contribute to the illusion that you, personally, are the center of the universe—the judge and the jury responsible for the conviction and punishment (at least in your own mind) of those you perceive to be guilty of having harmed you in some way. Forgiveness can be the ultimate liberation, one which opens the door to a stronger and more enduring faith.

"The ability to forgive and the ability to love are the weapons God has given us to live fully, bravely and meaningfully in this less-than-perfect world."

HAROLD S. KUSHNER: *When Bad Things Happen to Good People*

The emotional and physical benefits of forgiveness

Forgiveness can be essential for achieving mental clarity and objectivity. According to Fred Luskin (in *Forgive for Good: A Proven Prescription for Health and Happiness*), studies have documented that teaching people how to forgive can reduce depression and increase hopefulness, help with managing anger and build emotional self-confidence, develop a sense of spiritual connection, and heal wounded relationships. Learning to forgive is good for your mental and physical wellbeing as well as for your relationships, says Luskin. People who are more forgiving report fewer health problems and have fewer physical symptoms of stress. On the other hand, failure to forgive can be a risk factor for heart disease.

Be selective in your memory

Every historian knows that the past is what you choose to remember. You have it within your power to determine whether or not you had a happy childhood, whether your teachers and schoolyard playmates were helpful or harmful, whether you were accepted or alienated. The past is what you choose to remember. Choose yourself a good one. As Rita Mae Brown said, *"One of the keys to happiness is a bad memory."* (A personal note: I once had a teacher tell me, in front of the entire class, that I would "never amount to a hill of beans." That did not do much for my self-esteem, and for years I blamed that teacher. Today I realize that, far from trying to humiliate me, he was trying to motivate me, and all else having failed, resorted to this.

The paradox of forgiveness

Here's the ultimate paradox of forgiveness: the person being forgiven is not the person being helped; quite to the contrary, that person probably couldn't care less whether he or she is being forgiven—it's the person doing the forgiving who benefits. And in the same way, holding a grudge usually does nothing to harm the person against whom the grudge is being held, but that grudge can be emotional poison for the person who holds it. Forgiveness really is good for your soul—and for your health and happiness as well.

Real leaders are healers

Following his victory at Yorktown, George Washington allowed the British to surrender with dignity, and began the long process of healing his war-ravaged nation. After taking Lee's sword at Appomattox, Ulysses S. Grant extended generous terms to the former secessionists in an effort to begin healing the deep wounds that would scar his country for generations to come. After engineering the unconditional surrender of Nazi Germany, George C. Marshall oversaw the Marshall Plan to rebuild the nations of his former enemies. It's no wonder that each of these warriors and healers went on to hold important leadership positions for their country.

> *"The hand of a king are the hands of a healer."*
>
> J.R.R. TOLKIEN: *The Lord of the Rings*

Vengeance has a penchant for biting back

In November of 1918, the allied powers, led by France and Britain, finally defeated Germany in the most destructive war the world had ever seen (World War I). The Treaty of Versailles left Germany not just defeated but impoverished, humiliated, and hopeless. And fertile soil for the Nazi thugs who would within a few short years seek their own revenge (re-vengeance). Fortunately, following World War II the allies adopted a policy of forgiveness rather than one of revenge—even though Hitler's Germany was far more deserving of retribution than was the Germany of Kaiser Wilhelm. The humiliated children of the Kaiser's generation grew up to be war-makers and concentration camp guards. The forgiven children of the Fuhrer's generation grew up to work in factories and offices and go home at night to their children. Is it any wonder that forgiveness gets such high marks in the world's religious scripture (not to mention mental health textbooks)?

Be a Dionarap with prospective forgiveness

Assume good faith and expecting the best from others, and giving them the benefit of the doubt when you don't see it? To be a Dionarap (the word paranoid spelled backwards) means to engage in prospective forgiveness, to assume the best of everyone, no matter what they do or say. To get the chip off your shoulder and to flow more easily through life. Even to forgive people for things they never did and never will do (how many of us waste precious emotional energy by mentally thrashing somebody else for the things they *might* do?).

 ## Rules for the Journey

1) The paradox of forgiveness is that it's not given for the benefit of the person being forgiven. The real beneficiary is the one doing the forgiving, the one who is finally laying aside the twin burdens of anger and hatred.

2) Forgiveness often begins with forgiving yourself. As tough as it can be to forgive others for their crimes and sins, it can be even more difficult for us to forgive ourselves. The failure of self-forgiveness is a major cause of low self-esteem, and of anemic dreams and goals for the future.

3) To forgive does not necessarily mean to condone or to forget.

4) In your journal, make a list of all the past grudges and grievances that you've been hauling around in the backpack of your life. Considering the costs and "benefits" of each, ask yourself: is it worth it?

 ## Take-home exercise: Bury a rock in the desert

When I go with a group into the Grand Canyon, I will ask everyone to pick up a rock and carry it around in their backpack, letting it represent some emotional deadweight that they wish to leave behind when they come out. At the end of our trek, we build a cairn (a cairn is a pile of rocks that marks a trail). Everyone places their rock on the cairn and publicly says goodbye to it, then walks away.

I've seen some amazing—even miraculous—things happen, but nothing more wonderful than someone leaving behind a toxic grudge. If you're being eaten up with anger and hatred and nothing else has worked, try this. Carry around a rock, preferably in a back pocket where it causes you pain every time you sit down. Let that rock represent the painful memory/emotion. When you're ready, give that rock a funeral. Bury it, or put it on a cairn in the desert, and walk away from it. One of the reasons it's so hard to set aside our grudges is that they're invisible, and it's hard to fight what you can't see. By using Metaphorical Visualization™ techniques such as this one, you can take charge of your emotions, bury a painful past, and start your journey toward a more meaningful and productive future.

 Extra credit reading

> *"If we cannot forgive, we end up crucifying ourselves on the very cross we construct for our scapegoats. Our hate will be the hatred in ourselves that we have repressed, and that hatred of others masking our own self-hatred will continue to crucify us in their name."*

MICHAEL H. CROSBY: The Seven Last Words

Something to think about

Carrying a grudge is like drinking poison in the hopes that it will hurt someone else.

Module #29
The Third Cornerstone of Faith is Love

"Love is patient, love is kind. It does not envy, it does not boast, it is not proud. It is not rude, it is not self-seeking, it is not easily angered, it keeps no record of wrongs. Love does not delight in evil but rejoices with the truth. It always protects, always trusts, always perseveres. Love never fails."

I CORINTHIANS 13:5-8

Our goal for this module

To gain an awareness of how and why love is an integral element of faith, and to appreciate that genuine love is not a mushy, gushy emotion, but rather that it entails real work and sacrifice on behalf of others.

The tiny redwing blackbird will attack far larger crows and hawks to defend the babies in their nests. This fierce protectiveness is a wonderful metaphor for love. True love is much more than a mere emotion. It means working hard, taking risks, and putting yourself on the line for the ones you love. But the power of love is incredible. The Beatles were right when they sang that there's nothing you can do that can't be done, and there's no one you can save who can't be saved—all you need is love.

The real meaning of Mark 9:23

My favorite Bible passage is Mark 9:23: *"All things are possible for one who believes."* As a student of leadership and motivation, I obviously like the implicit "believe and you will achieve" message. But there is a more powerful, more important, and often overlooked message, one that has profound meaning no matter what your religious beliefs are. In the story, a man asked Jesus to heal his son. The man explained that Jesus' disciples had tried and failed. *"Can you help?"* the desperate father pleaded. Jesus turned the question right back around—*"Can you help?"*—saying that all things are possible for one who believes. *"I believe,"* the man insisted, then said, *"help me overcome my unbelief."* Despite the fragility of his belief, the man's son was healed.

I don't think this is a story about religious belief. Jesus looked into that man and saw a heart filled with pain and doubt, and at the same time with love and hope.

He did not administer a litmus test of faith before he healed the man's son; he knew the man would have failed it. Had Jesus asked that father to sacrifice a goat to the almighty Zeus in order to save his son, he would have done it, and they both knew it. Nor do I think this story is about a miracle. Oh, for sure there was a miracle, but it was not the healing of the boy. Today, doctors treat seizure disorders every day, and we don't turn our eyes skyward and thank God for the miracle (at least not as often as we should). Even in Jesus' day, there were many other faith healers. Jesus himself often remarked that with sufficient faith, anyone could do what he did. The story of Mark 9:23 is ultimately about love. Jesus looked at the man and did not see a sinner to be rebuked, or a potential convert to be preached at. He saw a man who was in pain, and it touched his heart.

Later, when Jesus was alone with the disciples, they asked him why they had been unable to drive out the boy's demon. Jesus replied that the kind of demon which had possessed the boy could only be driven out by prayer. Yet surely the disciples *had* prayed as they laid on their hands; still they failed. Perhaps the missing ingredient in their prayers was love. Perhaps they were too worried about whether or not the man would convert to their beliefs, or were too anxious about what the crowd would think if they failed to heal the boy. To Jesus, these were superficialities. A father's love for his sick son, like a shepherd's love for his lost sheep, that was all that really mattered to him.

> *"All things are possible for one who believes."*
>
>   MARK 9:23

Love is not a gushy emotion

Love is not a gushy emotion, it is hard work. In his best selling book *The Road Less Traveled*, M. Scott Peck defined love as: *"The will to extend one's self for the purpose for nurturing one's own or another's spiritual growth."* Peck goes on to emphasize that love is a relationship in which both parties evolve (in this regard, the definition is similar to that of transformational leadership). He also says that the word "will" means more than desire, but rather a desire which has been translated into action. Genuine love is not something you fall into, he says, but rather a decision to make a commitment, "whether or not the loving feeling is present."

You increase love by giving it away

In her book *A Simple Path,* Mother Teresa wrote that the most horrible disease in the West was not some physical illness, but rather a lack of love. *"We can cure physical diseases with medicine, but the only cure for loneliness, despair and hopelessness is love."* The absence of love, she said, is a spiritual poverty that is exacerbated by our obsession with material possessions, having fun, and egoistic thinking. Norman Vincent Peale used to play a game with himself in which he would shoot "sparks of love" at complete strangers. He may or may not have actually brightened their days (he insisted that he often did), but one thing is certain—each time he "sparked" ("spark" is a great metaphor, isn't it?) someone else, he felt better himself. A hug is another great metaphor for what really matters in life, because the only way you can get a hug is by giving one away.

> *"The laws of love differ from the laws of arithmetic. Love hoarded dwindles, but love given grows. If we give all our love, we will have more left than he who saves some."*
>
> JOHN MARKS TEMPLETON: *The Humble Approach*

 ## Rules for the Journey

1) The Beatles were right! There's nothing you can do that can't be done, there's no one you can save that can't be saved, and all you need is love. They also added that it's within you and without you.

2) Appreciate that genuine love is not a mushy, gushy emotion, but rather that it entails hard work and sacrifice on behalf of others.

3) You increase love by giving it away; hugs are a great metaphor, because the only way you can get a hug is by giving one away.

4) In his book *Reawakening the Spirit at Work* Jack Hawley points out that fear and anger always go together. They feed on each other until you can't tell them apart. They will destroy your objectivity and eventually your freedom of decision and action. That's why it's so important to confront your fear with courage, and to calm your anger with love.

5) One of the most emotionally corrosive words is "hate." Be careful how you use it, because it is malignant. The more things you "hate," the more your subconscious will view the world as a hateful (and thus frightful) place.

 ## Take-home exercise: Do a reality check on what really matters

Make a list of the things that are most important to you, the things that really matter. Now go back through your calendar and checkbook register for the past year and calculate the percentage of your time and money devoted to these "important things that really matter." Be totally honest—as you learned in junior high gym class, when you cheat, you only cheat yourself. There will, of course, be a pretty serious gap between your stated priorities and what the proverbial Man from Mars would have surmised based on how you spend your time and money (if there's no gap, call the Vatican to see if you've already been nominated for sainthood). The point is not to dump a load of guilt on yourself for past decisions, but rather to empower yourself to make more solidly values-based decisions about how you allocate your resources in the future.

 ## Extra credit reading

"Good management is largely a matter of love. Or if you're uncomfortable with that word, call it caring, because proper management involves caring for people, not manipulating them... You as a manager must trust people to do their work. You must take them at face value and let them know you believe what they say and you believe that they will do what they say they'll do."

JAMES A. AUTRY: *Love and Profit*

Something to think about

There are far too few words for "love." I'm saying very different things when I say *"I love my wife,"* or *"I love my work,"* or *"I love hot dogs."* What are the things you love, and what words would you use to describe that love?

Module #30
The Fourth Cornerstone of Faith is Spirituality

"No coward soul is mine/No trembler in the world's storm-troubled sphere/I see Heaven's glories shine/And faith shines equal, arming me from fear."

EMILY BRONTE

Our goal for this module

Understand that spirituality and religion are two distinct, though related, qualities, and that there is a place for both in our world and in our lives.

> **Have you ever tried to push a nail into a board with a hammer? It's pretty hard work, if it can be done at all. In order to drive that nail into the board, the hammer needs to recoil—to rest—to generate the force required for the task. That's a great metaphor for the task of caring for your soul. You must make the time for the spiritual in your life. You must make time for your soul. Especially in the western world, we've diminished the importance of soul-work, and have dichotomized the inner, spiritual world from the outer, material world.**

Spiritual faith and worldly wellbeing

Extensive research has shown that spiritual faith plays a large role in health and healing. People with a strong sense of spiritual faith tend to be more highly service oriented, to have more solid belief in themselves and in their dreams, to be more resilient in the face of adversity, and to be more committed to the success of others. They are more resilient in the face of adversity. In his classic 1902 book *The Varieties of Religious Experience*, William James wrote: *"How can it possibly fail to steady the nerves, to cool the fever, and appease the fret, if one be sensibly conscious that no matter what one's difficulties for the moment appear to be, one's life as a whole is in the keeping of a power whom one can absolutely trust?"* Good question!

The eternal battle between ego and soul

From the earliest stirrings of human consciousness, we have been aware of the inner conflict between our best and worst selves (angels and devils within). I think of it as a constant and ongoing struggle between Ego and Soul. When I'm living up to my best self and my highest ideals, Soul is calling the shots. All too often, however, I find that Ego is in control, with its "what's in it for me" attitudes (I suspect you find the same thing yourself). One of the greatest challenges in life is to subdue Ego sufficiently so that you can appreciate genuine spiritual experiences, but to do so without falling into the trap of debilitating guilt and low self-esteem (which is usually just another manifestation of Ego doing its dirty work).

Faith and prayer

In what has been called "the age of anxiety" prayer can be a compass and a rudder (for example, see Robert Gerzon's *Finding Serenity in the Age of Anxiety*). And the greatest antidote to this anxiety might well be the practice of praying. People can argue about whether you are actually talking with God, or simply carrying on an inner communion with your own conscience. Some of the people who have wrought important changes in our world not only believed that they were talking to God, they were quite certain that God was talking back (Joan of Arc and Florence Nightingale both come to mind). What cannot be argued is that for many people, prayer is an important source of strength in adversity and courage for achievement.

> *"The function of prayer is not to influence God, but rather to change the nature of the one who prays."*
>
> SOREN KIERKEGAARD

Listen for answers

When you do pray, don't forget to listen for the answers. If somebody believes enough to ask a question in prayer, does it not stand to reason that they might perceive an answer if they're paying attention? (As implied in the following Nugget of Wisdom by McZen, the answer might not be the one you wanted to hear, but it will usually guide you toward doing the right thing).

> *I pray for wisdom,*
>
> > *am answered with a study guide.*
>
> *I pray for strength,*
>
> > *am answered with an exercise routine.*
>
> *I pray for courage,*
>
> > *am answered with a call to commitment.*
>
> *I pray for generalities,*
>
> > *am answered with specifics.*
>
> MCZEN

Make peace with yourself

Ralph Waldo Emerson wrote that the only peace is that which you find within yourself. Here are six steps for giving yourself the gift of peace.

Let go

At least for a while, give up the need to be in control. You have challenges enough trying to control your own thoughts and emotions. Don't try to control what other people think or do, and don't worry about what they may think of you. It's a waste of energy that you can't afford to spare.

Surrender

Have faith that God put you on Earth for a reason, to serve a purpose, and that you will be given the guidance and the resources you need to fulfill that mission. When you pray, ask that *"Thy will, not mine"* be done. You may find that the resulting dreams are bigger and more splendid than any you could have imagined on your own.

Be receptive

Guidance will come from the most unlikely sources—your dreams, a chance encounter, a magazine article. Keep your eyes and ears open, and have expectancy. Opportunity doesn't knock; it's always standing outside your door, waiting to be let in.

Do what you love

Follow your dreams and to be happy. In a society that has been shaped by powerful traditions of Jewish suffering, Catholic guilt, and Protestant work ethic, this is no easy task.

Flow

Listen to your heart as you work. Discover those activities that command your attention so intensely that you forget the very passage of time.

Create meaning

Believe there is meaning to life—even when it seems to be capricious and malicious—and that you have a purpose in life.

Expect a miracle

Every great accomplish was once an impossible dream requiring nothing less than a miracle for its fulfillment. We have all been in desperate straits where it seemed our only salvation would lie in a miracle, and somehow survived. It is well for us to periodically look back on those situations where we were blessed with such miracles, and to look ahead to the future with hope and expect additional miracles. In all the miracles he performed in the Bible, Jesus often said two things:

1) It was not his magic but rather the faith of the person being healed that created the miracle; and

2) that whatever he did, any of us could do if we had sufficient faith.

Whatever one's religious beliefs, faith can be a powerful source of courage and optimism, which in turn creates self-fulfilling prophesies masquerading as miracles. It is important, however, to understand what a miracle is and what it is not:

> *"A miracle is not a magic trick. It is the bringing about of a change that would previously have been thought impossible. A miracle is not an event. It is a process. A miracle is not a gift. It is something earned through hard work and painful introspection. A miracle is not free. It comes with strings attached, and if you're not willing to share it, you will be unable to keep it."*
>
> JOE TYE: *Never Fear, Never Quit:*
> *A Story of Courage and Perseverance*

 ## Rules for the Journey

1) Spirituality and religion are two distinct, though sometimes related, qualities, and there is a place for both in our world and in our lives.

2) You will be helped by many people on your path through life. Don't believe that they came into your life by coincidence. You will also have many opportunities to help others. Don't believe that those needing your help came to you by coincidence.

3) Faith is the antidote to fear. When things look darkest, faith in yourself and in your mission will keep you going forward.

4) Expect a miracle but don't give God a deadline.

5) God's is a big tent, and there is room in that tent for people of all beliefs; the deepest faith is often reflected by those who honor the faiths of others without trying to impose their own beliefs upon them.

Take-home exercise: Restore the Sabbath in your life

Our world is so busy and so full of noise that it's difficult to make time for quiet reflection and introspection. Yet this is the exercise a healthy soul demands. For a month or so, make a point of finding a quiet time and space every day, even if it's for only five or ten minutes, to think about the things that really matter. A mini-Sabbath. And then, no matter how busy you are (or think you are) make a point of finding a bigger chunk of time during the week for thinking, reading (not pulp fiction!), and writing in a journal. A midi-Sabbath. If all else fails, make the time by watching less television. Pay attention. In all likelihood, you will find that, not only do you have a greater sense of peace, you will be getting more (not less) done by giving yourself time to rejuvenate.

 ## Extra credit reading

"Once we begin to resolve our fears, we will create miracles. Miracles are not just supernatural events such as parting waters or levitation. Miracles are any and every act of love and forgiveness. These miracles, these everyday acts of love, are occurring all around us; we just haven't recognized them yet."

ROBERT ROSKIND: *In the Spirit of Business*

As Norman Vincent Peale pointed out, we tend to forget the last two words of the second great commandment: to love our neighbors *as ourselves* (perhaps that's why we often treat our neighbors so poorly). Treat yourself with the love, respect and compassion you would give your most venerated neighbor. You deserve it, and your neighbor will appreciate it.

Part 2

Taking Effective Action:
Core Action Values 7 - 12

Core Action Value #7: Purpose

Core Action Value #8: Vision

Core Action Value #9: Focus

Core Action Value #10: Enthusiasm

Core Action Value #11: Service

Core Action Value #12: Leadership

"The most pernicious aspect of procrastination is that it can become a habit. We don't just put off our lives today; we put them off till our deathbed. Never forget: This very moment, we can change our lives. There never was a moment, and never will be, when we are without the power to alter our destiny. This second, we can turn the tables on Resistance. This second, we can sit down and do our work."

STEVEN PRESSFIELD: *The War of Art: Break Through the Blocks and Win Your Inner Creative Battles*

Core Action Values 7-through-12 are give you a roadmap for getting things done in the world. High achievers are always driven by a sense of Purpose that is greater than simply trying to make a living, and they have a Vision for the future; they Focus their time, money, and energy on what it takes to bring about that ideal future, and they do it with Enthusiasm and a commitment to Service; and in doing all these things they become the sort of person that other people want to follow—they become Leaders.

Core Action Value #7 is Purpose

Your work is the hammer and chisel with which you carve the statue that will be the future you. The work a person chooses to do, and how they choose to do it, is a key determinant of who they become.

Cornerstone #1: Aspiration

Purposeful people aspire to work that gives them a personal sense of meaning, and to making their corner of the world a better place.

Cornerstone #2: Intentionality

Positive thinking is planning and working to make it happen; wishful thinking is hoping and waiting for someone else to make it happen.

Cornerstone #3: Selflessness

People inspired with a sense of purpose rise above *"what's in it for me?"* thinking and commit themselves to a larger good.

Cornerstone #4: Balance

Purpose as a value means being purposeful in every dimension of life, not just in the work you do—also family, community, and personal growth.

"Purpose is that deepest dimension within us—our central core or essence—where we have a profound sense of who we are, where we came from, and where we're going. Purpose is the quality we choose to shape our lives around. Purpose is a source of energy and direction."

RICHARD LEIDER: *The Power of Purpose: Creating Meaning in Your Life and Work*

Module #31
Core Action Value #7 is Purpose

"The outward work can never be small if the inward one is great, and the outward work can never be great or good if the inward one is small or of little worth. The inward work always includes in itself all size, all breadth, and all length."

MEISTER ECKHART

Our goal for this module

To appreciate the power of having a guiding purpose in life, and to at least begin the process of thinking about what that purpose should be in your own case.

I once told a friend about my plans to hike up one of Colorado's fourteeners (mountains that are higher than 14,000 feet). She looked at me incredulously and asked, *"On purpose?"* It was a humorous moment, but as I thought about it, there was a deeper meaning in the exchange. To hike a mountain trail, or to undertake anything else, "on purpose" implies that you are doing it for a reason, and that doing it somehow ties in with a larger sense of purpose. To do something "on purpose" also implies a more substantial commitment to complete the task, even if it means making sacrifices, even if it means asking for help, even if it means that you might take a risk and make the effort and come up short.

The Dilbert Disease epidemic

The *Dilbert* comic strip drawn by Scott Adams is one of America's most popular, which is a sad commentary on our society. No doubt, Adams is a genius of biting satire, and some of the barbs he slings at corporate America are well-deserved. Many of us have experienced the indignities of being treated like cogs in the machine by the likes of the pointy-haired boss. But few of us also recognize that the "hero" of this strip, Dilbert, is a very sick man.

You see, Dilbert hates his job, can't stand the boss or the people he works with, and spends his most productive energies trying to avoid being given any real work to do. Yet his biggest fear is that he might lose the job he so virulently despises. That's neurotic! *Really* neurotic. Even worse, Dilbert is miserable because he *chooses* to be miserable. He chooses to play the role of the cynic, the martyr, the victim—to be part of the problem instead of being part of the solution. Fortunately, Dilbert doesn't seem to have a family, because if he did, you can imagine the negativity he would bring home to dump on his wife and children at the end of each day; you can imagine what negative, bitter people those kids would probably grow up to be, and the self-sabotaging attitudes they would bring with them into the world of work ("work sucks and then you die").

The Ecclesiastes prescription cures Dilbert Disease

In his book *When All You've Ever Wanted Isn't Enough*, Harold Kushner recounts the biblical story of a man known as Ecclesiastes, and how he walked down one dead end after another in his quest for happiness and peace. Neither wealth nor wisdom, parties nor prayer, gave meaning to his life. So where, in the end, did Ecclesiastes find the prescription for giving meaning to his life? It was through his work: *"Whatever your hand finds to do, do it with all your might"* (Ecclesiastes 9:10). That's ultimately the cure for Dilbert Disease. It's not something "out there"—a bigger job, more money, being empowered by your boss. It's something within: finding the joy in your work, whatever that work might be, then sharing that joy with others. Making your work, in the memorable phrase of Kahlil Gibran, "love made visible."

Don't wait for God to "call" you to a powerful and prestigious Mission. Chances are, you will not find the cure for cancer, win the Nobel Peace Prize, or become an overnight billionaire. Whatever work is before you—caring for patients in the nursing home, managing a corporate department, greeting customers at Wal-Mart, cleaning floors—"do with all your might." Don't do it to please the boss, don't do it for the paycheck. Do it for yourself, because at the end of the day, it is the work you have done, and the spirit with which you have done it, that will give meaning to your life. That is the ultimate lesson of Ecclesiastes, and the cure for Dilbert Disease.

Why is "over-achiever" a put-down?

The Bible asks why anybody would put a basket over a candle. Unfortunately, it's something many of us do on a regular basis. We all have an inner spark of magnificence, which we often subdue for fear of standing out. From very early school days, we have learned not to be an apple-polisher, a brown-noser, a curve-wrecker, a quota-buster—in short, to not be an "over-achiever." Misery loves company, but so does mediocrity. We want to fit in, so we put a basket over our inner candle, we cover up our spark, and we run the risk of ending up being both miserable and mediocre. To hold to "purpose" as a value means to live up to your true and full potential, to take the basket off your candle, even if it means being criticized by those who choose to hide their own brilliance under the basket of mediocrity as they criticize you for being an "over-achiever."

Mission versus calling

These two terms are often confused. Here's how I define the difference.

A calling is externally given. It's something you are born with (as Mozart was with his musical calling) or that comes to you unbidden from God or some other outside source of inspiration (as was the call Joan of Arc received to save France from the English).

A mission, on the other hand, is internally-driven. It's a decision to commit yourself to your work heart and soul, not just hand and head. A sense of mission often emerges only gradually over a period of time, not in a blinding flash of light. It's often quite unglamorous, especially at first. Mother Teresa toiled through many anonymous years of caring for the destitute untouchables of India before she began to gain international recognition for her work.

One other important factor is this: for most of us, it's probably too late to expect that we're going to experience one of those flash of brilliant white light callings to greatness. It is never, however, too late to develop a sense of mission. Ray Kroc was 54 years old when he first laid eyes on the McDonald's restaurant that defined the rest of his life's mission. Grandma Moses was 78 years old when she first picked up a paintbrush, yet by the time she died at 102 she left a treasure of artistic masterpieces.

See your work as the hammer and chisel with which you carve the statue of YOU

Remember how in Core Action Value # 1, Authenticity, we spoke of visualizing your ideal character and then creating it? Well, if you think of the future "you" as a statue, then the work that you choose to do, and the way you choose to do that work, becomes the hammer and the chisel with which you craft the statue of "you." A central premise of the *Bhagavad-Gitâ* is that the wise person works for the joy of the work itself, without attachment to outcomes, results, or rewards. In this way, one surmounts the ego and grows in wisdom and awareness, while setting an example that helps to lead others along the right path. Similarly, the *I Ching* admonishes us to do each task for its own sake, making it perfect, without worrying about pay or praise. This attention to the work is the foundation of excellence that ends up bringing about the pay raises and the praise which cannot be obtained by direct effort.

Flow and the joy of work

Flow is the mental state of being so engrossed in what you are doing that you lose track of everything else—what other people think of you for doing it, whether you will be successful or not, even the passing of time. It is a state of total immersion in an activity, of working hard and enjoying it for the sheer joy of the work. Flow is a common experience of peak performers. Dr. Mihaly Csikszentmihalyi, a professor of psychology at the Claremont Graduate University, has written a number of books on the subject, including *Good Business: Leadership, Flow, and the Making of Meaning*. These are the elements he defines for the optimal experience of flow.

1) A mission that inspires you.

2) Goals that have been selected because they are personally fulfilling, not because they're calculated to please others or make a lot of money.

3) Defined interim goals that provide immediate feedback on your progress.

4) Determination, self-discipline, and willingness to make short-term sacrifices to achieve long-term goals.

5) Total concentration and immersion in the effort, forgetting the egoistic self,

outside worries and cares, the opinions of other people, and the potential for material reward.

6) A sufficient block of time to really get involved in the work.

7) Teamwork—involving other dedicated people in your goals.

8) An external focus on the world, rather than a preoccupation with your own inner thoughts and emotions.

Dr. Csikszentmihalyi says that flow is the most intrinsically rewarding mental state, and that the opportunity to experience flow is more powerfully-motivating than pay raises, promotions, or little gold stars. As he writes in *Good Business*, our TV-saturated consumer culture has devalued anything labeled "work" and replaced it with an emphasis on relaxation and the acquisition of material things. As a result, he says, *"no matter how exciting and fulfilling a job may be, we confront it with a generalized bias against work learned early in life."* The challenge is to create meaning in your work, to commit to making a contribution, to have a mission and not just a job.

 ## Rules for the Journey

1) Purposeful people are positive thinkers who expect the best from themselves and from others, and who are willing to make any contribution necessary to the successful achievement of their work.

2) From very early school days, we've learned not to be an apple-polisher, a curve-wrecker, quota-buster or over-achiever. We want to fit in, so we put a basket over our inner light. Living with purpose is a challenge to remove the basket, to look inside and see the magnificent light that you have been hiding within yourself. It's a challenge to let that light shine through in your beliefs, your attitudes, and your behaviors.

3) Pursue your work with a sense of mission rather than concern for wealth or prestige, dive into your work with passion and make it your special joy to master the details, and empower yourself to perform at the highest levels of expectation and accountability. Wealth and prestige will take care of themselves.

Take-home exercise: Write a Purpose Statement and a Mission Statement

A purpose statement is a broad overarching statement that addresses the questions such as, *"Why I've been put on Earth, what really matters to me, and what are the most important priorities in my life."* It is overarching, covering both your work and other dimensions of your personal life. My own purpose statement, for example, has to do with helping people respark the spirit of mission in their work and the spirit of adventure in their lives. This overarching purpose applies to my roles as a coach and teacher, and to my roles as husband and father.

A mission statement, on the other hand, is specific to a certain mission. You might have separate statements for your family life, your career, and community service. The mission statement for my work with Values Coach, for example, has to do with teaching values-based life and leadership skills. This covers my work as a writer, speaker and coach. It helps to guide how I spend my time and resources. If, for instance, I were to be offered a high-paying, high-prestige job in my former career of hospital administration, I would immediately decline, because it is not "on purpose" with my mission.

As you write these statements, remind yourself that the thinking provoked by the process is more important than the final product, and that whatever you come up with will be written on paper, not carved in stone. And remember, your statements do not have to be perfect and they do not have to be final. In fact, they will be neither.

 ## Extra credit reading

"Individuals committed to a vision beyond their self-interest find they have energy not available when pursuing narrower goals, as will organizations that tap this level of commitment."

PETER SENGE: *The Fifth Discipline*

Something to think about

Someone with a job is never secure; someone with a calling is never unemployed.

MC ZEN

Module #32
The First Cornerstone of Purpose
is Aspiration

"There is a space between man's imagination and man's attainment that may only be traversed by his longing."

KAHLIL GIBRAN

Our goal for this module

To encourage you to raise your sites and expectations for yourself, and to make the commitment to translate those aspirations into effective action.

Were it not for aspiration and the related attribute of ambition, you would not be reading this because I would not have written it. In fact, but for aspiration—the desire to create something beyond what exists in the present world—we would all be out in the fields and forests hunting and gathering as did our prehistoric ancestors.

You are the beneficiary of the aspirations of previous generations, so make a point of adding to the legacy

Every blessing of your life today is the result of someone else's aspirations. Every meal you eat, every song you sing, every book you read, the car you drive, the house in which you live, the electricity that powers the house in which you live, the food you eat—it's all been made possible by the fact that at some point in the past someone, somewhere aspired to be someone, to create something that was new and special. To assume purpose as a personal value, then, means to aspire to add to that amazing collection of contributions that in the aggregate have shaped our world.

It's not about dying with the most toys

You might have seen the bumper sticker that reads, *"Whoever dies with the most toys wins."* It's hard to imagine a more superficial and vacuous approach to life, isn't it. Yet in the materialistic and status-obsessed (and drowning in debt) developed world, it's hard to escape the conclusion that, whether they admit it or not, many people actually feel that way. But true purpose-guided aspiration is not about having more stuff. It's about having a more authentic life, and contributing to making this a better world.

Aspire to authenticity

The comedian Lily Tomlin once said, *"I always wanted to be somebody…Now I realize that I should have been more specific."* The foundational aspiration is that to become the person you were meant to be, to do the things you were born to do. Which brings us back to Core Action Value #1, Authenticity. The more clear you are about your authentic best self and the strengths and passions of that best self, the more powerful and compelling will be your aspiration to become that best self. This in turn will lead you to more effectively pursue your most authentic goals and dreams.

Aspire to make a difference

Angela Theriot had a dreadful experience when she was admitted to a San Francisco hospital in 1978. But she didn't just complain about it, she decided to make a difference for future hospital patients. She started an organization called Planetree (named for the sycamore tree under which Hippocrates taught his students about medicine). Her dream was that hospital patients everywhere would see themselves, and be seen as, empowered partners in rather than passive recipients of their care. Today, more than one hundred hospitals around the world have adopted the Planetree philosophy of patient-centered care, and many others have been influenced by Planetree to change their practices. The aspirations of this one determined woman truly are, to quote a mission statement from Planetree flagship Griffin Hospital, "changing the face of healthcare."

Allow yourself to be touched by the world

Some of the noblest aspirations are sparked by allowing your heart to be touched by the needs of others. In his book *Three Cups of Tea: One Man's Mission to Promote Peace…One School at a Time* (with David Oliver Relin), Greg Mortenson tells of how a chance encounter with the people of a tiny village at the foot of the mountain he was trying to climb led to a life-changing and lifelong commitment to building schools for the children of Pakistan and Afghanistan. He was touched by the poverty of such villages, and by the lack of opportunity available for children (especially girls) raised in ignorance, and probably a bit surprised by how desperately the village elders wanted the schools he promised to build. If you let down some of your defenses, when you make yourself more vulnerable to the calling of the world around you, it just might spark a higher aspiration in you, the way it did for Greg Mortenson.

Aspiration leads to inspiration

"Dream no small dreams for they have no power to move the hearts of men." This phrase by Johann Wolfgang von Goethe might well be one of the most often-quoted passages in motivational books and speeches. When you have a big dream, when you aspire to be something, do something, create something that is magnificent, it moves your heart, and in moving your heart can move the hearts of others as well. From the dream of putting a man on the moon to the dreams of finding a cure for cancer or ending the scourge of war, people who aspire to change the world in a positive way tend to become more self-motivated and in motivating themselves, more effective at inspiring others.

Aspiration is the antidote to apathy and complacence

You probably don't have gills or razor-sharp teeth, but in one respect at least, you are like a shark: you have to keep swimming. The day you stop moving forward, you start to die. People with no goals, with no aspirations, sink into the emotional swamp of boredom and apathy, they become complacent and self-satisfied or, worse yet, they begin to feel like helpless victims because no one else is making their fantasies come true for them. This is one of the reasons that experts in goal-setting advise you to write down your goals every day and to keep them in front of you. They will inspire you to aspire to be and do more than you are now.

Be realistic—expect miracles

Every great accomplishment was once thought to have been something that would require a miracle. History is studded with examples of real-world miracles being made. From putting a man on the moon to paying off the last credit card, humans have proven themselves capable of achieving what once seemed impossible—capable of creating miracles. In fact, I would go so far as to say that if you are not aspiring to create miracles yourself, you might well be selling yourself short by settling for anemic dreams and goals.

 ## Rules for the Journey

1) Effective aspiration is the difference between wishful thinking and positive thinking. Wishful thinking is hoping for something and waiting for someone else to do it for you; positive thinking is *expecting* something and then doing the work necessary to bring that dream of today into the reality of tomorrow.

2) If no one aspired to a better world, we'd all still be hunting and gathering!

3) *What would you do if...?* Build a bridge from where you are now to where you want to be in your ideal future.

4) Purpose-guided people are positive thinkers who expect the best from themselves and from others, and who are willing to make any contribution necessary to the successful achievement of their work.

5) Purpose-guided people engage in positive thinking and don't delude themselves with wishful thinking.

 ## Take-home exercise: Aspire as if you could not fail

I have a coffee mug in my office that asks, *"What would you do if you knew you could not fail?"* It is a variation on the instruction that Winston Churchill gave his generals during World War II, to act as if they could not fail. If you knew that, whatever you were to undertake, you could not fail, what would you aspire to do? Before you write down some ridiculous thing such as win the lottery, remember the old admonition to be careful what you pray for; most people who win the lottery or otherwise stumble into unearned wealth end up broke and miserable. What would you be doing to become your authentic best self and to make the world a better place if you knew that you could not fail?

Extra credit reading

"The most important distinguishing trait of visionary leaders is that they believe in a goal that benefits not only themselves, but others as well. It is such a vision that attracts the psychic energy of other people, and makes them willing to work beyond the call of duty for the organization."

MIHALY CSIKSZENTMIHALYI: *Good Business: Leadership, Flow, and the Making of Meaning*

Something to think about

The greatest failure is not to strive for great things and fail to achieve them, but rather to have no dreams at all.

Module #33
The Second Cornerstone of Purpose is Intentionality

Whatever your hand finds to do, do with all your might.

ECCLESIASTES 9:10

Our goal for this module

To appreciate that to be a person guided by purpose means moving from wishful thinking to positive thinking, and to make that personal commitment that we will not just *try* to achieve our goals, but we will steel ourselves with the *intention* to achieve them.

One day several years ago I was driving into Page, Arizona for a Spark Plug training program with the hospital in that community. As I drove into town, I saw big yellow tractors gouging a hole in the desert floor. I later asked someone what was going on. *"That's going to be the new Super Wal-Mart"* was the reply. Now, for better or worse, that new store was all but a reality, even though all I could see was the incipient hole in the ground. On some desk in an office at Wal-Mart headquarters in Bentonville, Arkansas there was a set of blueprints and a budget, and sitting at that desk was a person who fully intended to transform those documents into a real bricks-and-mortar building. The power of intention creates memories of the future—it transforms the dreams of the present into the reality of the future. Today, where there was once a bare desert floor on the outskirts of Page, there now sits a Super Wal-Mart.

There is no try

I occasionally will have someone say to me, *"I'm going to try to be at your next Spark a Dream workshop at the Grand Canyon."* I've learned that the most appropriate response is for me to reply, *"That's too bad. We'll miss you."* This is because virtually without exception, anytime someone says they're going to "try" to be there, what they're really saying is that they'd like to come—providing it's not too difficult, too expensive, too inconvenient, or that something better doesn't come along. In one of the *Star Wars* movies, Yoda the Jedi master, says to Luke Skywalker, *"Do or do not—there is no try."*

In his book *You Can't Afford the Luxury of a Negative Thought*, Peter McWilliams says: *"If you think you want something and you're not actively involved in getting it, you're probably just kidding yourself."* Any time you hear someone complaining about something rather than working to resolve whatever it is that they're complaining about, chances are pretty good that they are engaged in this form of self-delusion.

Mixed motives are a good thing

Motives are the underlying "why" behind intention. You *intend* to do something because you have motives for doing it. And although the term "mixed motives" sometimes has a negative connotation, in fact it's not a bad thing at all to have multiple reasons for intending to do something. Here's a personal example. People sometimes ask me why I write. It's not a simple answer. I write partly because I enjoy the simple physical act of writing—the feel of a good pen moving across a clean yellow pad, the click of the keys on a keyboard. I also write in the hopes that what I write will encourage and inspire others. But I wouldn't be telling the whole truth if I didn't also say that I enjoy the recognition that comes from having been a published author, and it would be a flat-out lie for me to say that I didn't really like to receive royalty checks from the publisher. The reason it's good to have multiple sources of motivation is that together, they can inspire your intentions more powerfully than one single source of motivation.

When in doubt, go forward

There is a scene in J.R.R. Tolkien's fictional classic *The Hobbit* where Bilbo Baggins becomes separated from his dwarf companions in the cave of the goblins. He stopped to think for a bit, but could only think of how hungry and miserable he was. Then he considered his options. The way behind was blocked by goblins, and on both sides were the stone walls of the tunnel. His only option, Bilbo concluded, was to press on ahead. Having a sense of purpose might not prevent you from being hungry and miserable, nor will it relieve you of occasional doubt and anxiety. One thing it can do, however, is keep you from backsliding and waffling, and help you maintain forward momentum when the going gets tough.

Have a bias for action

In their landmark book *In Search of Excellence*, Tom Peters and Bob Waterman listed "a bias for action" as one of eight characteristics of excellent companies. Today, Peters says that this one characteristic is the only one to have really stood the test of time. Most creative people do have a bias for action, and if you want to become more creative yourself, one way to do it is by acting sooner and faster on your ideas. In surgery residencies, the motto is often *"see one, do one, teach one."* In the fast changing world of today, the most successful organizations will be those which experiment, build prototypes, try things, and keep what works and fix what doesn't.

 Rules for the Journey

1) Be a positive thinker, not a wishful thinker.

2) In one of his best-known sayings, management guru Peter Drucker wrote that wherever he finds important work being done, behind the scenes there is "a monomaniac with a mission." People who merely have a job merely make money; people with a sense of purpose make a difference.

3) The attitude you bring to your work is the most important choice you make on a daily basis. That choice defines the excellence with which you do your work, the impression you make on people around you, the perceived quality of your

work, the personal and career goals you set for yourself, and whether you are happy and fulfilled in your work, or chronically stressed-out, burned-out, and put out.

4) Do or do not (there is no try); pay attention to your vocabulary and replace wishy-washy words with words that convey purpose and expectation.

 ## Take-home exercise: Love the work more than the job

James Autry, author of *Love and Profit: The Art of Caring Leadership* and other books on business and leadership, once wrote that in his executive career, he had needed to fire people who'd loved their jobs (the title, the paycheck, the status, etc.), but that he had never had to fire anybody who loved the work itself. Take a moment for introspection and honestly ask yourself where you find your greatest joy—in the job or in the work. If your answer is the job, then you have an attitude problem. And the ultimate victim of your attitude problem is not the organization where you work, it's you yourself.

 ## Extra credit reading

"Regardless of what anyone might say to you, the truth about your feeling purposeful is that only you can know it, and if you don't feel it in that inner place where a burning desire resides, it isn't your purpose... Forget the aptitude-test results, forget the absence of skills or know-how, and most important, ignore the opinions of others and listen to your heart."

WAYNE W. DYER: The Power of Intention: Learning to Co-Create Your World Your Way

Something to think about

You tend to get what you expect out of life; positive intention can create positive self-fulfilling prophecies.

Module #34
The Third Cornerstone of Purpose is Selflessness

"We are formed and molded by our thoughts. Those whose minds are shaped by selfless thoughts give joy when they speak or act. Joy follows them like a shadow that never leaves them."

BUDDHA

Our goal for this module

To understand that to internalize purpose as a value means rising above "what's in it for me" thinking, and appreciate the paradox that the best way for you to achieve your goals is often first helping other people achieve theirs.

A great real world example of selflessness is Ray Kroc, who at the age of 54 began the process of transforming a single McDonald's restaurant into a worldwide fast food empire. For his first eight years, Kroc did not personally draw a paycheck from the company. Everything went back out to helping his franchisees become successful. Toward the end of his life, when Kroc was asked which of his many achievements he was most proud of, he would always reply that he had helped more people achieve their dreams of financial independence than anyone else who'd ever lived before him. By placing their interests before his own, he also built an incredibly loyal team of franchisees. Ironically, by not pursuing his own gain, but instead committing himself to helping others succeed, Kroc became one of the world's wealthiest men.

Be part of a cause that is bigger than you

People with a sense of mission seek more from their work than just a paycheck and benefits; they want to make a meaningful contribution—to their organization, their coworkers, and their community. And we see again the ancient paradox that the more one gives away, the more one makes a contribution without expectation of return, the greater the return will be. Here is a paradox that has been put forth in most spiritual traditions: to find yourself you must lose yourself, to save your life you must lose your life. In part what that means is that people who connect themselves to a bigger cause than their own success and welfare "lose themselves" to the mission, but in a larger sense "find themselves" through the work and the relationships involved with the mission. As the great scholar of myth Joseph Campbell once wrote, when you stop thinking about yourself (ego) and devote yourself to a bigger cause, a truly heroic self transformation (soul) will take place.

Cultivate a support group environment

"To have a friend, be a friend," said Mark Twain. One of my personal dreams is that every workplace would take on some of the characteristics of being a support group. Whenever I am speaking with members of a support group, I'm struck by the fact that almost never does anyone go home in a worse frame of mind than they arrived—they are almost always uplifted with the hope, courage, inspiration and examples of other support group members. Now, if people can be uplifted by sharing stories about such tragedies as cancer or a head injury or the loss of a child, why on earth can't we make the workplace environment just as uplifting? What if our mutual commitment was that we would not allow any individual to go home worse than they came in at the beginning of their work shift?

Exchange the spotlight for a floodlight

In his book *Sacred Hoops*, Phil Jackson describes how the Chicago Bulls evolved from the one-man Michael Jordan show of the late 1980s into the dominant NBA team of the '90s. The process began when Jackson told Jordan that the sign of a great player was not how many points he personally scored, but rather how much he contributed to elevating the performance of every player on the team. They implemented a new offense that gave other players more scoring opportunities. The rest, as they say, is history. Jordan proved not only to be one of the greatest players in the history of the game, but also emerged as a real leader who helped his teammates be leaders, not just supporting cast on The Michael Jordan Show. And the Bulls went on to win six national titles over the next ten years.

Tear down the silo walls

One of the most serious barriers to creativity in organizations is what's known as "the silo effect." Every department or division is in its own little silo, insulated from every other department or division. That's a real problem, because one of the greatest sources of creativity and innovation is sharing of ideas between units within an organization. You can do your part for tearing down the silo walls where you work. Simple things. Like, walking to another department instead of calling on the phone. Inviting people from other departments to your place for an orientation and a tour. Periodically sitting with different people in the cafeteria. When it comes to tearing down the silo walls that divide our organizations, familiarity breeds confidence—in yourself and in your coworkers. Not only that, you'll find that getting out of your box (on the organization chart) and getting out of your ego is one of the best ways to meet new people and make new friends.

 ## Rules for the Journey

1) Here's a paradox found in most spiritual traditions: **to find yourself you must lose yourself, to save your life you must lose your life**. People who connect to a bigger cause than their own success "lose themselves" to the mission, but in a larger sense "find themselves" through the work and the relationships involved with the mission. As Joseph Campbell put it, when you stop thinking about yourself and devote yourself to a bigger cause, a truly heroic self transformation takes place.

2) People with purpose seek more from their work than just a paycheck; they want to make meaningful contributions—to their organization, coworkers, and community. It's the ancient paradox that the more one contributes without expectation of return, the greater the return will be.

3) Selflessness is the foundation of real teamwork; purposeful people are more concerned about getting the job done than about getting credit.

4) When you see the job description as a floor and not as a ceiling, you'll be astonished at the opportunities that open before you.

Take-home exercise: Be an extravagant tipper

You have no doubt heard that it is more blessed than to receive, and that as you give so shall you receive. And I suspect that you smiled, said "that's nice," and filed the aphorism away with Santa Claus and the other fairy tales of childhood. If that's the case—if you would like to believe that giving is the best way to open the door to receiving, but you really don't believe it—please try this experiment. It will cost a bit of money, but nothing more than you can afford. It's a simple habit that, if you stick with it, will profoundly transform your view of yourself and of the world. Here it is:

Become an extravagant tipper. Not a generous tipper—an *extravagant* tipper.

If your breakfast bill is six dollars, leave a ten dollar tip. If you hand over a five dollar bill for a cup of coffee, leave your change in the tip cup. When you check out of a hotel room, leave a twenty dollar bill on the bed for the housekeeper. For you, this will be a minor expense; for a single mom working two jobs to support her family, it might well be the highlight of her entire day. I predict with great confidence that three things will happen. First, after the initial twinge of regret at having lightened your wallet, you will feel good about yourself. Second, this attitude of generosity will begin to permeate other areas of your life as you think less about what's in it for you and more about what you can do for others. And third, as a direct result of the first two outcomes, in ways that could never be predicted or explained, you will begin to experience greater abundance in your life (including, perhaps, the monetary variety). This will not happen overnight, but if you think of it as a lifetime habit rather than a one-shot experiment, the return on your investment will be extravagant.

Extra credit reading

"The most important distinguishing trait of visionary leaders is that they believe in a goal that benefits not only themselves, but others as well. It is such a vision that attracts the psychic energy of other people, and makes them willing to work beyond the call of duty for the organization."

MIHALY CSIKSZENTMIHALYI: *Good Business: Leadership, Flow, and the Making of Meaning*

Something to think about

Whatever you most need in life, the best way for you to get it is to help someone else get it who needs it even more than you do.

Module #35
The Fourth Cornerstone of Purpose is Balance

"Happiness is not a matter of intensity but of balance, order, rhythm and harmony."

THOMAS MERTON

Our goal for this module

To seek a sense of purpose in every dimension of your life—personal and professional, financial and temporal, physical and mental, emotional and spiritual.

No one on their deathbed ever said *"I wish I'd spent more time at work"* or *"I wish I'd watched more television"* or *"I wish I'd bought more lottery tickets"* or *"I wish I'd won more arguments."* It is just as important, if not more so, to have a sense of purpose in your personal and family life, in your financial and spiritual interests, as it is in your work life.

Integrate your work and your life

Leadership authority James Autry wrote that after a career of asking himself how he could balance his life and his work, he realized he'd been asking the wrong question, and that the right question was how could he *integrate* the two. How can you integrate your life and your work rather than trying to keep them in separate boxes? For example, if you are a manager working on a budget, you could ask your child to double check your figures, thereby giving him or her the opportunity to feel useful, learn something about what you do, and gain some experience at a real world skill that will come in quite handy later in life. You will obviously want to triple-check your child's arithmetic!

Replace "OR" with "AND" in your thinking

One of the qualities that the visionary companies described by Jim Collins and Jerry Porras in their book *Built to Last* was that they replaced "the tyranny of OR" with "the genius of AND." Not "low cost OR high quality" but low cost AND high quality." This is a shift of mind set that can help you be more creative. It's the difference between scarcity thinking (OR) and abundance thinking (AND). Think about how coming up with possibility-creating new answers to these old questions can change your life:

> *How can I get ahead in my career AND have more quality time with my family?*

> *In my role as a manager, how can I simultaneously enhance productivity AND morale within my area of responsibility?*

> *How can I save and invest for my retirement AND make generous donations to my favorite charities AND have a rich and enjoyable experience of life now and not put it off to some future date (e.g. after I retire)?*

Here's a simple example, from my own experience. Every year, I spend a week hiking in the Grand Canyon. Because I already have most of the gear I need, my total expense is several hundred dollars. In Las Vegas or Orlando, I could blow through that much before lunch on the first day. For me, a week in The Canyon is far more rewarding than a week spent standing in a crowded line waiting for a mechanical ride, and also allows me to be more responsible in my personal finances. That's one way that I can transform an OR into an AND.

Have fun on the job

In their book *Lessons from the Top*, Thomas Neff and James Citrin interviewed 50 of America's top business leaders about their secrets to success. There were, of course, a number of common themes in their responses to questions about what it takes to build a great business. One might surprise you; having fun. Almost all of these leaders think it's important for people to be enthusiastic, passionate, and excited about their work—and to have fun on the job. Being enthusiastic and having fun generates energy; being bored and miserable destroys energy. By changing your attitudes, perceptions, and behaviors, there are almost always ways you can bring a little more enthusiasm and fun into your job. The payoff will be more energy to do the job well and to do it fast, meaning more time to have fun off the job as well.

Know when to back off

One day early in the development of the world's first super computer, the team was stumped by a particularly vexing problem. Inventor and company founder Seymour Cray came into the room where his colleagues were agonizing over possible solutions and said, *"Let's go tubing."* The computer technicians filled up their cars with inner tubes, snacks, and liquid refreshments and headed for the river. After an afternoon of playing in the sun, they came back with renewed enthusiasm and a fresh perspective. The problem was quickly resolved. The wise leader recognizes those times when the logical thing to do is to work harder, but the brilliant thing to do is to stop working and go for a joyride.

 ## Rules for the Journey

1) Seek a sense of purpose in every dimension of your life—personal and professional, financial and temporal, physical and mental, emotional and spiritual.

2) In his book *Creativity in Business*, Michael Ray says we should do only that which is "easy, effortless, and enjoyable." Which of your activities meets the 3-E test, and what can you do to more fully engage in them.

3) Take care of yourself physically, including getting the sleep you need, so that you have the energy to experience the joy of life in every dimension.

4) Be vigilant about not putting yourself into double-bind situations (that's the psychologist term for a self-imposed lose-lose condition); the parent who brings home work and feels guilty for not playing with the kids, so then sets aside the work to play and feels guilty for not getting the work done, has put him or herself into a no-win position.

Take-home exercise: Go back to kindergarten

Several years ago, I was listening to the radio on my way to work, and heard a story about a very creative woman who had established a very creative business—an adult kindergarten. That's right! Every Saturday, people would come to her "school" and relive kindergarten—finger-painting, story time, cookies and milk, even the afternoon nap. There was a waiting list to get into her program. Every kindergarten kid thinks he or she is creative, don't they? Yet surveys show that only two percent of the adult population thinks of themselves as being creative. Perhaps if you were to devote a Saturday to finger-painting, reading children's stories, and yes, even taking a nap, you could remember that vital something about yourself that you forgot so long ago—the inner creative spark that made you so unique. It's still there, that spark. Go in and find it.

 ## Extra credit reading

"Some people today suggest that this search for meaning and identity has resulted from having too many choices, rather than too few. Instead of becoming a gateway to freedom, our wealth of options tether us to a dilemma. And this conundrum echoes through our leisure and free time experiences."

MARTIN KIMELDORF: *Serious Play*

Something to think about

Earlier in this course I asked you what you would do if every job paid the same and had the same social status (a whopping good question). Now I'll ask you this: *If every job paid the same and had the same social status, how would it affect the way you spend your time?*

Someone who is "on a mission" becomes a force of nature—unstoppable. Your underlying Purpose is what makes sure that you define the most appropriate and important missions upon which to launch yourself.

Core Action Value #8 is Vision

Humans are the only creature that can see something in the mind's eye that is invisible to the body's eyes. Cherish this God-given gift—cultivate it, use it to create your ideal future.

Cornerstone #1: Attention

What you choose to give your attention to will create the platform upon which you create your future vision—choose wisely.

Cornerstone #2: Imagination

Visualization is the active process that precedes the creation of vision; don't abuse your imagination with fantasy and worry, but rather use it to create memories of the future.

Cornerstone #3: Articulation

Before your vision can become reality, it must be articulated in such a way as to inspire passion and confidence in those who must contribute to bringing that vision into being.

Cornerstone #4: Belief

Belief is a force of nature. All achievement begins in the mind of someone who believes in the possibilities.

"Cherish your visions; cherish your ideals; cherish the music that stirs in your heart, the beauty that forms in your mind, the loveliness that drapes your purest thoughts, for out of them will grow all delightful conditions, all heavenly environment; of these, if you but remain true to them, your world will at last be built."

JAMES ALLEN: *As A Man Thinketh*

Module #36
Core Action Value #8 is Vision

"The tragedy of life doesn't lie in not reaching your goal. The tragedy lies in having no goal to reach. It isn't a calamity to die with dreams unfulfilled, but it is a calamity not to dream... It is not a disgrace not to reach the stars, but it is a disgrace to have no stars to reach for. Not failure, but low aim is sin."

BENJAMIN ELIJAH MAYS

Our goal for this module

To appreciate how the interaction of vision and visualization can help transform the dream of today into the reality of tomorrow.

The day before he died of lung cancer, Walt Disney was in his hospital bed detailing his ideas for the layout of Disneyworld in Orlando for his brother Roy. He asked Roy to imagine the landscape that in his own mind he was painting on the ceiling of his hospital room. Roy put off an already long-delayed (and much-deserved) retirement to see his brother's project through. At the grand opening several years later, someone remarked to Roy that it was too bad Walt wasn't alive to see the finished park. Roy simply replied that Walt had, in fact, seen the finished park.

The power of vision

Without vision, the Book of Proverbs tells us, people perish. With vision, it might have added, they can prosper. Vision, said Jonathan Swift, is the art of seeing the invisible. Every great accomplishment was once the "impossible dream" of a dreamer who refused to be deterred. Until the dream has become real in the mind of the dreamer, it's unlikely to ever be manifested in the outer world. Once it has become a concrete mental image, a memory of the future, though, it's only a matter of time and effort before it makes the transition from impossible dream to great accomplishment.

Vision and visualization

Let's distinguish between "vision" and "visualization." Vision is a noun—a mental image of the desired outcome, an ideal future reality. Visualization is a verb—a mental rehearsal, a vivid mental motion picture in which you watch yourself going through the steps that will create that future state. Vision and visualization work together hand-in-glove. Here's how it works: you imagine a dream of some sort—the ideal job, the business you wish you could start, the perfect vacation, whatever. Then you visualize yourself doing the things you would have to do in order to transform that dream of today into your reality of tomorrow. As you see yourself doing those things, the dream becomes more real, more tangible, and far more likely to make the transition from mere daydream to concrete goal.

An authentic vision of the future rarely comes as a sudden epiphany. Rather, it is typically the culmination of a process of reading, networking, thinking, and dreaming that coalesces into a mental image of a desired future reality. Not only that, vision is never final. The mind's eye can only see so far down the road and through the mist. When Walt Disney first dreamed of Disneyland, the notion of the Epcot Center, or of building parks in Paris or Tokyo, was part of the vision yet to evolve.

The Vision Hourglass

If your dream is sufficiently big and wonderful, you probably have no idea of how you will ever be able to make it come true. That's okay—in fact, it's to be expected. The bigger the dream, the more imponderables are likely to lie between here and there. It's what I call the "vision hourglass." You have a pretty clear picture of where you are today, with your hourglass filled with the sands of the future. And you can paint a grand picture of where you want to be at the other end, once all the sands of time have taken you into the future. What you can't see is everything that will happen in between. It's sort of a black box labeled "miracles happen here." You can be sure of two things. First, if you keep working at it, those miracles are likely to happen, though you can't see the precise way in which they will happen. Second, if you don't do anything, nothing will happen. This brings us to an important point: creating a vision is a physical as well as a mental activity. Taking action—building a prototype, writing a business plan, talking to people who have already done something similar—all help to refine, and to expand, the vision. It's not enough to just see it, you also have to work at it!

The Vision Hourglass

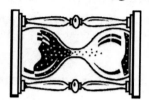

If you have some idea of what your ideal future is (CEO, Maui condo, writing a novel, etc.), you can be clear about a one-year goal that will begin to move you in that direction.

With imagination, you can generate a widescreen vision pf where you want to be in 7 or 10 years, at the distant end of thehourglass.

The long stretch of time between accomplishment of this year's goal and realization of the eventual dream is like the narrow waist of the hourglass, where vision becomes constricted. This is the "black box, expect a miracle" phase of the journey.

From the seed grows the tree

The *I Ching*, that ancient book of wisdom, reminds us of how important the first few steps of any journey are, because they profoundly influence the eventual destination. Take a step out of a front door in Chicago and head west. Turn twenty degrees left, you'll eventually end up in Los Angeles. Turn twenty degrees right, you'll eventually end up in Seattle. Sometimes the biggest difference between the entrepreneur who builds a thriving enterprise like Starbucks and the owner of the corner coffee shop is simply the vision with which they each started.

Victims live in the past, visionaries live in the future

Are you a victim or are you a visionary? You cannot be both simultaneously. Victims are mired in the past; visionaries are focused on the future. Trying to be a visionary while at the same time complaining about how you have been victimized by people or circumstances of your past is no more possible than trying to inhabit two different rooms at the same time. Any time you find yourself complaining— about anything!—you are living in the past. If you want to dream bigger and more achievable dreams, replace complaining with gratitude, and replace pessimism and worry with optimistic expectancy.

Rules for the Journey

1) Don't waste your imagination on worry and fantasy; instead, exercise it and employ it to create the vision of the future you want to create and are willing to work to achieve.

2) Distinguish between "vision" and "visualization." *Vision is a noun*—a mental image of the desired outcome, an ideal future reality. *Visualization is a verb*—a mental rehearsal, a vivid picturing of you going through the steps that will take you to that future state. Vision and visualization work together hand-in-glove to help you create your future.

3) As Lao Tzu said more than two thousand years ago, the longest journey begins with a single step. You don't need to have a detailed plan for everything that happens subsequently, but you do know that you'll never reach your desired destination if you don't take that first step, and then keep walking.

4) Are you a victim or are you a visionary? You cannot be both simultaneously. Victims are focused on the past; visionaries are focused on the future. Trying to be a visionary while at the same time complaining about how you have been victimized by people or circumstances is no more possible than trying to inhabit two different rooms at the same time.

Take-home exercise: Write your autobiography in advance

Write a prospective autobiography as if it were an article to be published in a newspaper or magazine at some future time. Begin with a sentence that reads something like this one, taken from my own autobiography of the future: *"You wouldn't know it from the worldwide reach that Values Coach International has today, but ten years ago it was just Joe Tye and a few colleagues traveling the country to promote values-based life and leadership skills. Now, though, millions of 'Spark Plugs' across the globe are practicing the principles included in The Twelve Core Action Values. Here's how it happened..."* I've rewritten the story several times (in fact, if you've read my books *Never Fear, Never Quit* or *Your Dreams Are Too Small*, you'll recognize these as early drafts of my "memory of the future" for Values Coach), and over the years have seen the power of the self-fulfilling prophecy in action.

That's how it works. You begin with a statement that contrasts your ideal future state with the reality of your current state, as if the future state had already been achieved. Then you write the story of how that future ideal state came into being. Be sure to include reference to all the people whose help you required. For best results, use a desktop publishing program to make it actually look like it was copied from a real publication—for example, by including your photo of today with a caption that reads something to the effect that "the hero begins the quest." Post that article on your day-timer, on your bathroom mirror, and anywhere else that it will remind you and motivate you to transform your dream of today into a memory of the future.

 Extra credit reading

"I learned this, at least, by my experiment: that if one advances confidently in the direction of his dreams, and endeavors to live the life which he has imagined, he will meet with a success unexpected in common hours. He will put some things behind, will pass an invisible boundary; new, universal, and more liberal laws will begin to establish themselves around and within him; or the old laws be expanded, and interpreted in his favor in a more liberal sense, and he will live with the license of a higher order of beings... If you have built castles in the air, your work need not be lost; that is where they should be. Now put the foundations under them."

HENRY DAVID THOREAU: *Walden*

Something to think about

"Live your dreams before they come true, just in case you never wake up."

MCZEN

Module #37
The First Cornerstone of Vision is Attention

"If you would attain to what you are not yet, you must always be displeased by what you are. For where you are pleased with yourself there you have remained. Keep adding, keep walking, keep advancing."

SAINT AUGUSTINE

Our goal for this module

To appreciate that attention is our most precious resource, even more than time because it is how we choose to use our time, and to practice paying attention for the opportunities of today that are the foundation upon which dreams of tomorrow are built.

When Mark Thatcher was laid off from his job, he decided that what he really wanted to do most was kayak down wild rivers. But he also wanted a better lifestyle than one can earn by being a river guide. The answer was, quite literally, right there at his feet. He saw the need for a new sort of footwear specially-designed for aquatic and other outdoor sports. During his first year in business, he only sold about 200 pairs of the new sport sandals he'd invented. Today Teva, the company he founded, sells millions of sandals and other sporting gear around the world. He worked hard to build the business, but his success began with a simple act of paying attention.

Pay Attention!

It's often said that time is your most precious resource, but that's not true. Everyone has the same amount of time—it cannot be killed, it cannot be saved. Your most precious resource is not time, it's attention—how you choose to use your time. You can only pay attention to one thing at a time; it cannot be multi-tasked. The choices you make regarding how you allocate your attention will determine the opportunities you perceive for getting ahead and for making a difference, and will substantially determine your circle of friends and associates. Indeed, the precious and irreplaceable nature of attention is what underlies the phrase "*pay* attention," because you can only spend each moment's attention once. What you choose to pay attention to today will substantially define the boundaries of your vision for tomorrow.

Ultimately, you become what you pay attention to

Over time, the choices you make with regard to allocating your attention profoundly influence the kind of person you become. As Ralph Waldo Emerson famously put it, *"A man becomes what he thinks about all day long."* Pay too much attention to the news (which I call the tragi-tainment media, because their business is turning tragedy into entertainment) and you'll become a more frightened and anxious person. Pay too much attention to television sitcoms and you will ineluctably become more cynical and sarcastic. Pay attention to educational and inspirational books and tapes, though, and you'll become a more positive, self-empowered, and motivated individual.

Healthy dissatisfaction creates energy for change

Without healthy dissatisfaction, there's no motivation for change. Someone can be living like comedian Jeff Foxworthy's redneck—the house has wheels and the car doesn't—but if they're perfectly content with that situation, they're not going to be motivated to do what it takes to change the situation. Let me emphasize the word "healthy." Complaining about things that can't be changed, like the weather, or things you have no intention of working to change, like the U.S. tax code, is not healthy dissatisfaction, it's whining. Whining does more than drag you and everyone around you down into the emotional dumps. It also keeps your attention fixated on the negative circumstances that are all too easy to find, with the price being that you cultivate a negative vision for your future.

When somebody creates healthy dissatisfaction by dreaming new dreams and raising their expectations for their futures, it creates what psychologists call cognitive dissonance, which is trying to simultaneously hold two incompatible beliefs—there is a conflict between the current reality and the ideal state. It is a painful form of mental illness, one that most people seek to avoid. You can use this to your advantage, though, if you focus your dissatisfaction on what you can do to close the gap. As you become more determined to realize the dream, one of two things *must* happen: either the dream dies and becomes just a daydream, or the dream becomes a source of motivation that catalyzes you to take effective action. Think about the things that make you unhappy—the gaps between what you would like to see and what you actually do see. Are these gaps just a psychological nuisance, or do they cause you unbearable mental agony? Now, imagine how wonderful your life will be once you eliminate the cause of that mental agony—the gap between the reality of today and the dream for tomorrow.

 ## Rules for the Journey

1) Attention is the platform upon which dreams of the future are built.

2) Without a healthy dissatisfaction, there is no motivation for change. What is the *one* (and only one) thing you would most like to change in your life? How can you restrict your dissatisfaction so that it is entirely focused on that one thing and nothing else, not complaining about anything else, until it becomes a fire of motivation that propels you into action?

3) Remember, there is no free lunch. What is the price you will have to pay to achieve your dreams? Are you willing to pay that price?

4) If you're like me and everyone else in the world, your alarm clock never really finishes the job; there are parts of each day in which you are going through the motions on auto-pilot. Simple rituals (such as snapping a wrist bracelet or stopping every hour for a deep breath) can help you be more awake, aware, alert, and alive (the 4-As of Attention).

Take-home exercise: Find a need and fill it

"Find a need and fill it." That's the mantra of the entrepreneur, the social change activist, the person who wants to make a difference in the world. Here's a four-part exercise that can help you put your attention to work on laying the foundation for your future vision:

1) Think about a goal or a dream that's important to you—make the vision of that dream as real and as tangible as possible.

2) Take a look around; what does someone else need that, if you were to help them fill that need, could also move you in the direction of your dream (remember: the best way to get what you want is to help someone else get what they want).

3) Once you have identified that need, what is an action that you can take *right now* to help fill that need?

4) What will you have to give up in order to create the time and other resources necessary for you to fill that need (and will you make the commitment to make that short-term sacrifice in order to achieve the longer-term benefits)?

Extra credit reading

"If you pay attention at every moment, you form a new relationship to time. Your own absorption slows you down internally. The slowing down feeds your sense of deep appreciation and at the same time produces more energy. In some magical way, by slowing down you become more efficient, productive, and energetic, focusing without distraction directly on the task in front of you. Not only do you become immersed in that moment; you become that moment."

MICHAEL RAY: *Creativity in Business*

Something to think about

Why do you think people use the word "pay" rather than the word "loan" when asking for your attention? Because they are asking you to give them your most precious and irreplaceable resource—your attention.

Module #38
The Second Cornerstone of Vision is Imagination

"You can't depend on your judgment when your imagination is out of focus."

MARK TWAIN

Our goal for this module

To make more effective use of the unique gift that is your imagination, and to diagnose and overcome inner barriers to creative dreaming and big thinking.

> **Little Katie was drawing a picture of a tree in her kindergarten class when the teacher came over and looked down at it. *"Why, Katie,"* said the teacher, *"that's very pretty, but I've never seen a purple tree before."* Katie smiled up at the teacher and replied, *"Gee, that's too bad."* Why do we lose the ability to see purple trees? More important, what can we do to get it back?**

Dreaming and doing

If you can dream it, you can do it, said Walt Disney. Unfortunately, many of us have lost the capacity to dream. Imagination is like any other muscle—it becomes weak and atrophied if not used, but it can be built up with exercise. Imagination is more important than knowledge, said Albert Einstein. We spend years in school trying to fill our heads with knowledge. How many of us ever took even a single class on imagination? When was the last time you read a book on how to be more creative, on how to use our imagination more effectively? Go to the library, go online, visit the bookstore and read up on your most precious, most underused mental resource any of us possess—your imagination. *Think and Grow Rich* by Napoleon Hill is one of the bestselling self-help books of all time. Note the order of the words in the title—*think first*, then grow rich. Most of us have it the other way around—*"If I had more money, then I'd have time to think."* Especially in today's fast-paced and hyper-competitive world, your think ethic will be more important in determining your future success than your work ethic.

The five tools that big goals give you

Goals are the stepping stones by which the dream you imagine today gradually becomes the reality you will live with in the future. When you really believe in your goals, and when you are committed to working toward their fulfillment, they will give you the following five "power tools" which you won't get from timid little goals:

Compass

A big goal can be your true north. For example, if you truly want the dream house (true north), you'll spend a lot less time going "east" to watch television and spend a lot less money going "west" for some impulse shopping at Wal-Mart.

Magnifying Glass

A big goal has incredible leverage. When you are committed to a big dream, your efforts are magnified through everyone else who buys into that dream with you (friends, family, co-workers, and even, eventually, your banker).

Magnet

A big dream to which you are committed is like a magnet that attracts the people, money, and other resources needed for its fulfillment into your life (this is the well-known Law of Attraction).

Flywheel

A flywheel is the heavy metal disk that gives momentum to a car's engine in between the firing of each piston. In the same way, a big dream gives you momentum to power your way through the inevitable down days, obstacles, and setbacks.

Spark Plug

A big dream is to human achievement what a spark plug is to a car; it catalyzes action.

The paradoxes of big goals

A paradox is a statement that appears to contain an internal consistency, but which often points to a greater truth—like, *"to save your life, you must lose it."* It doesn't make literal sense, but has a deeper meaning when you really think about it. There are at least these three paradoxes internal to dreaming big dreams and setting big goals:

1) Big goals are often more likely to be achieved than timid goals, because they inspire people to work toward their achievement.

2) Relative to the potential reward, big goals often require a proportionately lower level of risk and effort than smaller goals.

3) Once fulfilled, big goals become the platform for even bigger goals (and might actually seem to be pretty small in retrospect).

"Define your future by your dreams and not by your memories, by your hopes and not by your fears."

Rules for the Journey

1) Mark Twain said you can't rely on judgment if your imagination is out of focus; how can you cultivate a better balance between left and right brain?

2) Creativity is something that can be cultivated. I love John C. Maxwell's definition of creativity: intelligence having fun. What can you do to take your intelligence to the playground?

3) Worry is imagining a horrible future that we do not want to have happen. Fantasy is imaging a beautiful future that we have absolutely no intention

whatsoever of working to bring about. While worry and fantasy can both be beneficial in moderation, if that's the only use you're making of your imagination, you are wasting this precious God-given resource.

4) Your dissatisfaction can be a great motivational resource, but only if you don't waste it on a lot of gratuitous complaining. If you allow yourself to be dissatisfied with one and only one thing in your life, and refuse to complain about anything else, you will generate considerable intensity toward your goal. You'll be like the person sitting on a thumb tack—thinking of nothing else but how to achieve your goal of changing seats.

 ## Take-home exercise: Exercise whole-brain dreaming

Let your subconscious mind work for you while you're asleep. Just before you drift off, plant a perplexing question, and when you wake up immediately write down all of your dreams. You may be surprised at what you discover; when Elias Howe was stumped in his work to invent a sewing machine, he had a dream in which warriors carried spears with holes in the points, giving him the idea for putting the threading hole at the tip rather than at the top of the needle. This dreamland epiphany finally broke the mental bottleneck. You can do the same thing. Put your subconscious mind to work on important problems while your conscious mind is sleeping. Before you go to bed, plant a question or a problem in your head, let it roll around as you fall asleep. Keep a notepad or recorder by the bedside and record your dreams as soon as you wake up. You just might find dreamland epiphanies of your own.

Extra credit reading

"The power of vision is incredible! Research indicates that children with 'future-focused role images' perform far better scholastically and are significantly more competent in handling the challenges of life. Teams and organizations with a strong sense of mission significantly outperform those without the strength of vision... Vision is the best manifestation of creative imagination and the primary motivation of human action. It's the ability to see beyond our present reality, to create, to invent what does not yet exist, to become what we not yet are. It gives us capacity to live out of our imagination instead of our memory."

STEPHEN R. COVEY, A. ROGER MERRILL,
and REBECCA R. MERRILL: *First Things First*

Something to think about

T. S. Eliot said that good poets borrow, but great poets steal. The greatest innovations are not new ideas, but rather the adaptation of extant ideas into a new arena. On this basis, anyone can be creative. All you need to do is pay attention, be curious, ask good questions, and figure out how you can borrow someone else's idea for your purposes.

Module #39
The Third Cornerstone of Vision is Articulation

"A rock pile ceases to be a rock pile the moment a single man contemplates it, bearing within him the image of a cathedral."

ANTOINE DE SAINT-EXUPERY

Our goal for this module

To appreciate the importance and the power of using words to create visceral mental images that transform dreams into memories of the future.

A picture might be worth a thousand words, but the ability to articulate a dream into words that paint a picture is far more valuable. When Martin Luther King created the vision of all our children living together in harmony, when John F. Kennedy crafted the vision of a man walking on the moon, when Millard and Linda Fuller built Habitat for Humanity upon the dream of a world in which there were no more shacks, they were each articulating a future in such a way that anyone could understand, and be inspired by, that dream.

Making the dream of today the reality of tomorrow

The ability to articulate a vision in such a way that it informs and inspires others is the difference between an idle dreamer and a true visionary. Articulation is the first step in a process that transforms a dream into a "memory of the future," a destination at which you have already arrived in your mind, and to which your physical arrival is only a matter of time and effort. Build your castles in the air, said Thoreau, then put foundations under them. *Imagination* is what you use to build those castles up there in the air. *Articulation* is what you use to build the foundations under them.

Transform your dreams into "Memories of the Future"

You can remember the future more clearly and more accurately than you can remember the past. Now, before you jump to the conclusion that I need to see a shrink, let me demonstrate. Try to remember your second birthday party, in vivid detail. You can't do it, can you? Even though you've been told it really did occur, there is a blank in your memory bank where your second birthday should be. Now, remember the future. Specifically, remember tomorrow. Get a clear mental picture of where you will be tomorrow—what you'll be wearing, what you'll be doing, who you'll be with. If you're like virtually everyone else, your memory of tomorrow is much clearer and more distinct than your memory of your second birthday, and many other past events. How about next week, can you picture that? Next month? Next year? One common characteristic of highly successful people is the ability to "remember" their goals and dreams into existence.

If you were about to drive to Tuscaloosa for your sister's wedding and had never been there before, the first thing you would do is consult a map and plan the journey. You are much more likely to arrive at the church on time than if you simply hopped in the car and started driving in the general direction of Alabama. Studying the map is a form of mental rehearsal that greatly increases the odds you'll be there for the big event. In the same way, transforming your dreams into a Memory of the Future is a mental rehearsal that greatly increases the odds you'll show up on time for your own celebration party. There are five sequential steps to creating a memory of the Future, which I call **"The 5-A's:"** **Articulation, Affirmation, Asking, Action, and Adaptation**. Let's say that your big dream is having that dream home. Here's how you can transform that dormant dream into a vibrant Memory of the Future:

Articulation

The first step is knowing what you want, and as specifically as possible. Can you articulate the dream? Instead of just "a big house" can you describe the ideal location (country or city); do you have a mental picture of the ideal floor plan; in your mind, can you feel the brass fixtures with your fingertips, smell the new carpet on the floor, and hear the wood crackling in the fireplace? The more vivid your mental image, and the more different senses and emotions involved, the higher the likelihood of achievement.

Affirmation

This step is vital, because we tend to dream in pictures but worry in words. You've got the picture of the dream house painted in your mind, but the negative little inner voice is saying, *"You can't afford the mortgage you have now, how are you gonna pay for that monstrosity?"* It's essential to counteract this negative self-talk with affirmations that are positive and nurturing.

Asking

Any dream of significance will require help from others, and the way you get that help is by asking for it. In the case of the dream house, for example, you will probably have to ask the bank for a mortgage. The best approach is to, very early in the process, go to the bank and share your dream, then ask: *"What do I have to do in order for you to give me the loan I need to make this happen?"* The bank is in the business of lending money, and your banker would love nothing better than to be in a position to approve your loan request. Let them help you make sure that they can say "yes" when the time comes.

Action

Without action, a dream is just a wish. Action is the acid test that determines the difference between a daydream and a memory of the future. But you don't have to do it all at once: small actions consistently applied can yield great accomplishments. Every time you do something, *anything*, in pursuit of your dream, even something as simple as setting up a savings account for the downpayment on that dream house of yours, you are reinforcing a future reality, a *memory of the future*, in your own mind, which is ultimately where the battle is won or lost. The secret is to do something *every single day*.

Adaptation

Finally, you must be willing to adapt to changing circumstances. In many cases, that will mean adapting *upward*. When John F. Kennedy announced the goal of putting a man on the moon, nobody could have foreseen the massive technological revolution that was unleashed as each accomplished element of that goal laid the foundation for new goals, and as dreamers and innovators adapted the previous progress to new aims.

The more you practice transforming your dreams into *memories of the future*; the more you exercise your mental muscles of attention, imagination, planning, and belief; the more authentic your dreams will become. Sometimes this will mean letting go of the dreams you have outgrown. I once dreamed of living in a big house; today I'm perfectly happy in our little farmhouse (but my dreams of making a difference in the world with *The Twelve Core Action Values* are much bigger than they were when I was dreaming of that big house).

Rules for the Journey

1) Become a more effective communicator, skilled in the arts of creating word pictures and mental images using metaphors and stories. Joining a Toastmasters Club or taking a Dale Carnegie class can help you put polish on your speaking skills.

2) Transform dreams into Memories of the Future with the 5-A's: Articulation, Affirmation, Asking, Action, and Adaptation

3) Couple "impossible" goals with "impossible" deadlines to create the sense of urgency that leads to inevitable results.

4) One of the most effective ways to *think big, start small (but start now)* is to get into the habit of thinking in terms of prototypes; virtually any dream, no matter how big, is amenable to being represented and tested with some form of a prototype.

Take-home exercise: A Great Idea: Categorize the reasons for achieving your goals

Make a list of the most important goals for the personal, family, career, financial, educational, service, and spiritual dimensions of your life. For each goal, write down your answer to these questions:

> *If I achieve these goals, what will be the benefits to myself, my family, my co-workers, and my community?*

> *What do I need that I don't have now (including education, resources, contacts, and personal drive) in order to achieve these goals?*

> *What are the reasons I deserve to achieve these goals?*

> *When I'm successful at achieving these goals, how will I share that success with others?*

> *What are the sacrifices I'm willing to make in order to achieve my goals, including the things I will give up to more effectively concentrate my energy, time, and money?*

You will find that having a strong understanding of the reasons you have for wanting to achieve your goals, the trade-offs that you will commit to make, and the benefits to be realized by you and others, can be a great source of motivation.

 Extra credit reading

"Regardless of the circumstance of your life, you are the writer, director, and producer of your mental images. You will always act out those pictures. Your circumstances do not determine what your life will be; they reveal what kinds of images you have chosen up until now. From the quality of your physical appearance, to your level of nutritional health, to the state of your financial holdings, to the quality of your relationships and everything else that requires an action by you, you are acting on images. Your mind stores away all of the images that you elect, and you daily carry out the assignments of those thoughts."

WAYNE DYER: *You'll See It When You Believe It*

Something to think about

When someone criticized Ludwig von Beethoven for writing music that required such forceful playing that it would destroy the piano upon which it was being played, he replied that he was not writing for the puny instruments of his day.

Module #40
The Fourth Cornerstone of Vision is Belief

"What the mind of man can conceive and believe, the mind of man can achieve."

NAPOLEON HILL

Our goal for this module

Understand that belief is a powerful force of nature, just as real for being invisible as the forces of gravity, magnetic attraction, and true love.

When Admiral DuPont reported to Admiral Farragut the failure of Union ships under his command to break into the Confederate-held Charleston harbor during the Civil War, he recounted all the excuses for not doing so. After DuPont had finished with his litany Farragut said, *"DuPont, there was one reason more."* And what, DuPont asked, might that be? Farragut replied, *"You did not break into the harbor because you did not believe you could do it."* The following year, Farragut himself demonstrated the power of belief. He had himself tied to the mast of his flagship as he led the Union fleet into Mobile Harbor. When one of his ships was sunk by a confederate mine, Farragut famously hollered, *"Damn the torpedoes, full speed ahead."* Mobile was taken that day.

The Power of Belief

I once had an aquarium that I stocked with a variety of cichlids, a particularly aggressive species of fresh water fish. The biggest fish immediately began to attack the smaller ones. I had to move him into a different tank for fear that he would kill his tank-mates. Some time later, while cleaning out his tank, I put the big fish back in the old tank with the smaller fish, keeping a watchful eye out to make sure that he didn't get violent again. But a fascinating thing happened. Not only did the bigger fish not attack the smaller ones, he actually cowered in one corner, while the smaller fish, who themselves had once themselves cowered in that corner, were now fearless in attacking this big intruder.

What had changed? The fish were the same size as they had been before, and they were swimming in the same water, but their roles of aggressive attacker and submissive victim had been totally reversed. It seems to me that the only way to explain this change in behavior is by understanding the altered belief systems of these fish (to the extent that fish can have a belief system). Before the transfer, the big fish believed himself to be the master of his aquatic domain, and acted the part, while the smaller fish acted the part of the beleaguered victims they believed themselves to be. But when I put the big fish back into the original tank, he now took on the role of stranger in a strange land, while the smaller fish had become the protectors of their "turf." This time I had to remove the big fish from the tank for *his* protection.

This is a great metaphor for the power of belief. Though it's invisible, belief is a very real force, one that can play a role in your life that is every bit as real as the role gravity, which is also invisible, plays in the universe. Positive, nurturing beliefs can keep you grounded within your authentic self and help you stay connected to your dreams of the ideal future. Negative, destructive beliefs—about yourself and the nature of the world around you—can cause you to act in ways that are incompatible with the achievement of your goals and dreams.

You'll see it when you believe it

Every great accomplishment was once the impossible dream of a dreamer whose belief overcame every obstacle and setback:

> *A man walked on the moon in John F. Kennedy's mind long before Neil Armstrong actually took that giant leap for mankind.*

When Ronald Reagan stood at the Berlin Wall and demanded that it be torn down, he could already visualize the rubble at his feet.

The computer on your desk existed in the mind of Steve Jobs at a time when even most computer professionals still thought Apple was just a piece of fruit.

Belief is a cosmic force very bit as real as gravity, magnetic attraction, and true love. Belief can open your mind to magnificent new vistas of the imagination. Belief can power you through the roadblocks, around the brick walls, and over the mountains that stand between you and the achievement of your dreams. Belief can transform individuals, build teams, and change the world. I would go so far as to say that nothing great can happen that has not first already happened in the mind of a great dreamer, and that once it has happened in that mind, it is only a matter of time before it happens in the world.

Don't lie to yourself

Any time you hear yourself uttering those toxic two words, *"I can't..."* remind yourself that you're probably not telling the truth. In all likelihood, the truth is that *you can*, but you don't want to, it would be difficult, it would be expensive, it would be inconvenient, or there are other things you would rather be doing. But here's the secret to turning that falsehood into a true statement—simply append the word "yet." When you say *"I can't yet,"* what you are really saying is *"I can, but first I need to (fill in the blank)"*. When you start doing whatever it is that you need to do first in order to prepare (learning new skills, saving your money, managing your time, connecting with new people, etc.), you start to erase that toxic "t" at the end of the magnificent word "can."

Be willing to suspend your disbelief

What's the first thing you must do if you want to enjoy the latest *Harry Potter* novel, or the latest installment in *The Lord of the Rings* movie trilogy? Suspend your disbelief. You have to, at least for the moment, forget that magic, wizards, and talking trees are ridiculous fabrications and let yourself believe that a small band of heroes really can save the world. Give yourself the same benefit. Most of us believe negative things about ourselves that simply are not true. We believe we're not capable of accomplishing great things, that we don't deserve to achieve the successes of which we dream. Begin by simply being aware of what your self-inhibiting beliefs are, and then challenging those beliefs. *"What old people say you cannot do, you try and find you can,"* said Henry David Thoreau. What your own inner critic says you cannot do, you try and find you can.

Hope + Ignorance = Power

In his book *The True Believer*, Eric Hoffer wrote that every successful mass movement must share two characteristics—incredible hope for a better future, and absolute ignorance of just how difficult the road will be in striving for that better future. You are probably not trying to start a mass movement, but there's an important lesson here, whatever your dream is. Hope for great things coupled with dismissal of the intervening difficulties is a source of great power for accomplishing "the impossible." This is why at the beginning of any new venture you should combine the hope of high expectations with a willful underestimation of the difficulties that might lie ahead. It's also why it's so important that you not listen to people who tell you that it will never work. Whatever the naysayers say, you are going to succeed—and you better believe it!

 ## Rules for the Journey

1) Vision becomes destiny; you'll see it when you believe it!

2) My favorite Bible passage is Mark 9:23—all things are possible for one who believes. I don't take that to literally mean that if I believe I can command a mountain to move, it will in fact move at my command. Rather, I take the story in which that verse appears to mean that if you confront your disbelief with courage and perseverance and take the first steps toward your authentic goals and dreams, you will find an incredible store of inner power as you move

forward with faith in the journey and in the outcome.

3) Reprogram negative self-talk and self-limiting images of who you are with affirmations and self-defining metaphors that are positive, nurturing, and affirming (and quite frankly, more likely to be true); after all, if you don't believe in yourself, how can you believe in your dreams; and if you don't believe in yourself, how can you expect others to believe in you?

4) Appreciate the incredible power of collective belief; one of the best ways for you to bolster your own belief is to inspire belief in the people around you.

 ## Take-home exercise: Write your own horoscope

You will have another great day to be working with a great group of people. A wonderful business opportunity will come from out of the blue today, but it won't be obvious, so keep your eyes open. There will be great news from home, and you'll be inspired in ways that could not have been predicted yesterday.

That was my horoscope the other day. Pretty good, huh? Of course, all my horoscopes are pretty good. That's because I don't take any chances—I write them myself. I stole the idea from Marc Myers' book *How to Make Luck* (T.S. Eliot said that good poets borrow and great poets steal—I do both). I typically write my own horoscope for the next day at night before going to bed; that way I can sleep on it. I often share the idea with groups when I'm speaking. *"It's a horoscope,"* I will say, *"not a to-do list, so be extravagant. Shoot for the moon. Wish for anything you want, from out of the blue, just so long as your wish is authentic. Then believe it will happen."*

What I'm doing with this seemingly silly exercise is encouraging people to dream bigger dreams, and then to hope for their fulfillment, knowing that hope is almost always an essential precursor to effective action. People are much more likely to take effective action if they are hopeful of success than if they expect to be disappointed. Several months after having conducted a leadership retreat in which

I prescribed this daily personal horoscope exercise, I received an e-mail from a participant who had written in her personal horoscope that a relationship with a long-estranged friend had been restored. That's all she did—expressed in writing the hope that a burned-down bridge would be rebuilt. Several days later, this woman got a phone call from the estranged friend inviting her out to lunch. It was, she said, a miracle.

I love the saying that coincidence is simply God's way of remaining anonymous. And I hear stories like this often enough to believe that it's more than random chance or dumb luck; miracles really do happen. Give it a try. Start writing your own daily horoscope. This can be an incredibly powerful visioning exercise, because when you write your horoscope (as opposed to writing down your goals), there are no limitations. It's like answering the question, *"what would I want to happen today if I could wave a magic wand and make it happen?"*

 ## Extra credit reading

> *"One of the most important expectations a leader must set has to do with the generation of optimism, hope, and aspiration, especially in the context of transformation, a change that unfolds over many years... This faith involves faith in oneself, in one's leaders, and in the process of transformation itself."*

EDWIN C. NEVIS, JOHN LANCOURT and
HELEN G. VARSALLO: *Intentional Revolutions*

Something to think about

"So many of our dreams at first seem impossible, then they seem improbable, and then, when we summon the will, they soon become inevitable."

CHRISTOPHER REEVE: *STILL ME*

You can remember the future more clearly and more accurately than you can remember the past: you have a much more clear and accurate mental picture of where you will be tomorrow than you do of your second birthday. The real secret of successful people is that they create memories of the future not just for tomorrow but for years down the road.

Core Action Value #9 is Focus

The One Big Yes requires lots of little No's. Focus is an essential ingredient for effectiveness, whether in your career or hobbies, your financial situation, or your personal happiness.

Cornerstone #1: Target

Be clear about what you really want, and don't waste time, energy and money chasing things you really don't want.

Cornerstone #2: Concentration

When you are clear about what you want, concentrate all of your resources—time, money, and energy—on that goal.

Cornerstone #3: Speed

Cultivate a sense of urgency for achieving your key goals.

Cornerstone #4: Momentum

It is much easier and more productive to keep yourself moving in a desired direction than it is to bog down and have to restart your engine.

"Every person and every organization is the product of a coalition and the forces within the coalition are always at war. The war is between the trivial many and the vital few. The trivial many comprise the prevalent inertia and ineffectiveness. The vital few are the breakthrough streaks of effectiveness, brilliance, and good fit. Most activity results in little value and little change. A few powerful interventions can have massive impact."

RICHARD KOCH: *The 80/20 Principle: The Secret to Success by Achieving More with Less*

Module #41
Core Action Value #9 is Focus

"Things that matter most must never be at the mercy of things that matter least."

JOHAN WOLFGANG VON GOETHE

Our goal for this module

Understand the incredible leverage that focused people have in achieving their goals, motivate you to become more focused yourself, and encourage you to think about your One Big YES and how you can distinguish activities required to make that happen from all of the Little no's that clamor for your time, attention, energy, and other resources.

The ruler of an ancient kingdom once called together all of the greatest scholars and tasked them to gather together all of the world's greatest wisdom for his library. It took several decades, but they finally had a library like the world had never seen. The king again called together his scholars, and explaining that he would never have time to read all those books, tasked them to distill all of that wisdom into one book. After many years, they brought their king the biggest book that had ever been written. The king looked at this book with dismay, and exclaimed that with his old eyes he would never be able to read it. *"Distill all of this wisdom into one sentence that can guide my decisions and actions,"* he commanded. After many more years, the scholars brought their aging king a parchment scroll containing that one sentence. The king unrolled parchment, and he read:

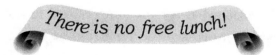
There is no free lunch!

The real secret of success

You can tell a lot more about what a people's real values are by looking through their checkbooks and calendars than by listening to them talk about their values.

When you're guided by values, your Big Dream is like a magnet drawing you toward the desired future, preventing you from heading down wasteful side roads, and helping you to maintain your forward momentum. Take the time to look through your checkbook and calendar; what are they saying about *your* values? No individual or organization can do everything well. Focus provides the discipline to target key goals and then to concentrate all available resources on the accomplishment of those goals. For individuals, focus will create more time and money to devote to the important things in life. For organizations, having a clear focus will enhance service and product quality, improve employee involvement and morale, and optimize operating productivity.

Travel light

It is unlikely that you will ever see a horse win the Kentucky Derby carrying a three hundred pound jockey. You can always travel more quickly if you travel light. You will build your dream house a lot sooner if you're not cluttering your life with all kinds of material things now. You will sooner achieve emotional equanimity and spiritual peace if you stop dragging behind you the dead weight of old grudges, regrets, fears, and anger. Complexity is the enemy of focus, and simplicity is it's ally. The more you can simplify your life—physically and emotionally—the sooner you will achieve the goals that really matter to you.

Focus and productivity

Most of us, when we hear the word "productivity" think in terms of business and finance, of doing more with less, of speeding up the assembly line. In fact, however, high productivity is essential to quality, both at the organizational level and the personal level. Southwest Airlines has the highest productivity in the airline industry by a substantial margin; it also has more celebrations, more parties, and more fun than all the rest put together. There is a direct cause-and-effect relationship here: Southwest Airlines can afford to have more fun because it is more productive, and it is more productive because its people have more fun. Furthermore, high productivity is often associated with high morale, and not the reverse. People like to know that their time is being used effectively, and for things that matter. The same factor work is at work at a personal level. One main reason some people have time to travel, go back to school, or engage in other activities for which the rest of us are unable to find time for is that they are more productive in taking care of the basics.

Focus and time

You have no doubt heard the rock, gravel, sand, and water theory of time. If you fill a beaker full of rocks, it is not full, because you can still add gravel to fill in the gaps. But it is still not full, because you can then add sand, and after that, water. That is a great metaphor for your calendar. You have big rocks (the annual strategic planning retreat, a trip to Key West), gravel (the weekly budget meeting, making rounds), sand (responding to emails and telephone calls), and water (waiting for the elevator). The story is now well-known of how J.K. Rowling went from welfare to billionaire on the strength of her *Harry Potter* books. And where did this single mother find time to write such incredible books? She made optimal use of the sand and the water. Waiting in a line, instead of complaining about her time being wasted, she made use of that time by writing a few more lines of her book. I think we would all agree that it was a pretty good trade-off, and a pretty good investment. Nobody on their deathbed ever said that they wish they'd spent more time watching television. The way to avoid someday having those regrets is to be more aware and judicious when it comes to the dribs and drabs of time, the sand and the water of your calendar, and putting it to better use.

> *"All we have to decide is what to do with the time that is given us."*
>
> J.R.R. TOLKIEN: *The Lord of the Rings (Gandalf)*

Focus and money

Each of *The Twelve Core Action Values* is essential. There are, however, times where one particular Core Action Value can have a disproportionate impact. For the person who is dealing with serious financial problems, the place to start is quite often with Core Action Value #9, Focus. Chances are that a lack of Focus contributed to that person's money problems in the first place (for an example of how this happens, see Aesop's Fable about the grasshopper and the ant). Read any book on how to get out of debt and more effectively manage your money and one of the key themes will be that you need to be seriously focused on the problem. Every nickel that leaves your household should be going to your highest priority (e.g. paying off the credit card debt instead of cable television and lottery tickets). The more focused your spending behaviors, the more wealth you will have in your future. And that is as close to an ironclad guarantee as you are going to get in this life.

Focus and Integrity

One of the most important ways people earn trust is by being reliable. And one of the most effective ways to make sure you are always reliable is to be focused. Here are 9 little words that will help you be more reliable:

Just say no: The more you say "no" to trivia, distraction, temptation, and other diversions from that which is important, the more you will have the time, money, and other resources you need to reliably meet your commitments and achieve your goals.

Just do it: Do the things that you might not want to do, but which must be done in order for you to achieve your greater goals.

Do it now: The beauty of Think Big, Start Small is that there is always some action that you can take—right now—to get things moving and to keep them moving.

 ## Rules for the Journey

1) Define your vision; the more clear and tangible it is in your mind and in your vocabulary, the more likely it is to become real in your world.

2) Focus your attention on what's most important; have a small, manageable number of key priorities at one time, then concentrate all possible resources on their achievement.

3) Don't be tempted by distractions. Learn to distinguish between a distraction and an unexpected but prudent opportunity to be pursued.

4) Don't allow gossip or idle chatter to distract your focus from key priorities.

5) Carry a book and/or a journal with you wherever you go. That way, if you're stuck waiting for an elevator or in a taxicab you can make good use of the time—and eliminate the number one excuse most people give for not reading or writing in a journal: that they don't have enough time.

 ## Take-home exercise: Be a status contrarian

A status contrarian is someone who feels no need to buy into the Madison Avenue borrow-and-buy treadmill, and who is perfectly happy being themselves without needing to "keep up with the Joneses." Take pride in the fact that you buy reliable used cars rather than always buying new (and seeing the value of your car drop markedly the minute you drive it off the show room floor). Make a trip to Goodwill before you head to the department store (you'll be helping the disadvantaged as well as saving money). Sam Walton drove a battered old pickup truck, and Warren Buffet lives in the same house in Omaha that he's always lived in. They knew that real status comes from accomplishments, not from accoutrements. Being a status contrarian will help you say "no" to all the tempting but diversionary ways to waste your time, money, and energy. If you get into the habit, you'll be amazed at the time and the money you save to invest in things that are far more important than trying to impress people you don't know.

Genuine status comes from accomplishments, not from accoutrements.

 ## Extra credit reading

"I don't think most people realize how stressful it can be to have multiple incomplete tasks hanging over your head... It has always intrigued me because often, it would be relatively easy and simple to bear down and complete something—not almost complete something, but really complete it 100 percent and get it out of the way... This is an easy habit to break. Take an honest look at your own tendencies. If you are someone who often almost finishes something, take note of the tendency and commit yourself to that last final completion. You can do it—and when you do, your life is going to seem so much easier."

RICHARD CARLSON: *Don't Sweat the Small Stuff at Work*

Something to think about

Don't chase what you don't want, don't want what you can't have, and appreciate what you already do have.

Module #42
The First Cornerstone of Focus is Target

→ →

"I have learned from years of experience with men, that when a man desires a single thing so deeply that he is willing to stake his entire future on a single turn of the wheel in order to get it, he is sure to win."

THOMAS EDISON

Our goal for this module

To explore specific goal-setting methods for identifying your most important priorities, to consider effective action strategies for staying on target to achieve those priorities, and to not waste time, money, and other resources on things that in the long run don't really matter.

If you saw the first *Star Wars* movie, you might remember the scene where a Jedi pilot is leading his squadron in an attack on the Death Star. He kept repeating this one command: *stay on target, stay on target*. It's almost impossible to stay on target if you don't know what your target is, or if you're trying to simultaneously hit fifty targets. The first step to being more focused is gaining clarity about what it is you really want—your target. This also means gaining clarity about what you don't want, so you don't end up wasting time and money shooting at illusory "targets."

Know what you really want

The bigger your goals and dreams, the more important it is to keep them on your mental front burner. But many of us feel like the circus performer trying to keep fifty plates spinning precariously atop sticks, frantically running from one to the other to keep them from crashing to the ground. That is a formula for frustration and ultimate mediocrity. But as Napoleon Hill wrote in *Think and Grow Rich*: *"There is no hope of success for the person who does not have a central person, or definite goal at which to aim."*

Don't chase what you don't really want

This sounds so simple, doesn't it? The problem is, most of us want everything. We even want things we don't want! For proof, you need look no farther than the attics, garages, and storage sheds filled with stuff we just had to have but now no longer need. All of this stuff represents a use of time, money, energy, and attention that was not devoted to achieving something of lasting significance. The problem is accentuated by our advertising-driven economy, a key function is which is to encourage us to want even more. We become like little kids at Christmas, rushing from one package to the next without stopping to play. Many people answer the question, *"What do you want?"* in much the same way that the Supreme Court defines pornography: *"I'll know it when I see it."* A much better approach is to crystallize in your mind those things which are truly important, to devote yourself to their achievement, and to not chase the things that you really don't want or to want the things you can't have.

Don't waste your time and money on trivial things

Which would you rather have in ten years: 1) a high degree of professional success, a feeling of pride in your education and accomplishments, and money in the bank; or 2) a flabby body, a mind full of useless trivia, and ten thousand dollars worth of receipts for the cable or satellite TV bill? Sounds like a no-brainer, doesn't it? Actually, it's a pretty accurate representation of the enormous gap that so often exists between what we say we want and the way that the proverbial Man from Mars would observe how we spend our time and money. Unfortunately, in the process of chasing what you don't really want, you end up depriving yourself of the things that you really do want.

The *One Big Yes* Requires lots of little no's

If you want to go back to school for an advanced degree, you're going to have to say no to your television set and surfing the internet for entertainment. If you want to save a down payment for your dream house, you're going to have to stop subsidizing Wal-Mart and Target by engaging in shopping therapy. *The One Big Yes* requires lots of little no's. But here's the payoff: self imposed short-term limitations lay the groundwork for long-term abundance and freedom. It's like the difference between having fun and being happy. Denying yourself opportunities to have short term fun can give you time and money to develop the skills and the resources that provide for great future happiness. To say "yes" to any one thing also means saying "no" to all of the alternatives. You can only spend an hour once, you can only spend a dollar once. You cannot both be a medical student and a beach bum in Hawaii.

The One Big
YES
Requires Lots of Little No's

 ## Rules for the Journey

1) The fewer goals you pursue at one time, the more goals you can pursue over time. But here's the payoff: self imposed short-term limitations lay the groundwork for long-term abundance and freedom. It's the difference between having fun and being happy. Denying yourself fun now gives you time and money to invest in future happiness.

2) As you know from the Serenity Prayer, there are many things beyond your control. While you certainly can't ignore such things (taxes comes to mind), the greatest use of your time, talent and resources is getting a focus on the things that you can control.

3) Successful people tend to be highly diversified in their skills and interests, but tightly focused on the achievement of high priority business and professional goals. How can you diversify and focus like this?

Take-home exercise: Identify the things you really don't want (but think you do)

I'm usually skeptical of books that promise a pathway to quick and easy wealth, but I read *Double Your Income Doing What You Love* because I have great respect for author Raymond Aaron. Having been a speaker at his Monthly Mentor programs in various Canadian cities, I've seen firsthand the results that his clients have achieved using the techniques he prescribes. Raymond himself has built a very successful business, and now takes one full week of vacation every month (he recently cross-country skied to the North Pole!). How did he, and how do his clients, achieve such great results? It begins by learning to say no. Raymond focuses his time on doing the few things he loves to do, and is really good at doing, and either delegates or does not do the rest of it. In his book, he shows how—by setting goals at three levels for minimum, target, and outrageous success—you can immediately begin to focus on those activities that will bring you that success. It's real world instant gratification, not the fantasy world variety.

Whatever your goals are, the most important starting point might well be for you to figure out what you think you want but really do not. You will need a small notepad. For the next week keep track of how you spend every hour and how you spend every dollar. At the end of the week, add it all up. Then ask yourself how much of your time and money was devoted directly to achieving your most important goals and how much went to more trivial things. With the insights you gain, make a list of things you might think you want at the moment, but suspect that someday you'll look back with regret at having wasted the time and money. For example, here are some of the things on my own *"thought I wanted but really don't"* list:

- ***Renting a DVD of every movie that was nominated for an Academy Award this year (it's not consistent with my big goal of reading more and finishing the book I'm writing).***

- ***Responding to emails every hour instead of batching them and dealing with it all at once toward the end of the day (it's not consistent with my big goal of giving my "prime time" concentration to projects that require the most creative thought).***

Eating a bowl of ice cream every night before I go to bed (it's not consistent with my big goal of being lighter and stronger for my next Grand Canyon hike).

Buying a new super-size flat-screen TV and connecting it to cable (it's not consistent with my big goal of maximizing time and money to invest in the Values Coach business).

 Extra credit reading

"How do you get everything done? Wrong question! How you get the most important things done? Right question. How you figure out which things are most important, how do you lay out your day, and how do you give some of your overflowing to-do list to others? Good questions."

WILLIAM BRIDGES: *Creating You & Co.*

Something to think about

Parents need to be willing to make sacrifices for their children to provide for their health, safety, and education. Think of the future you as a child of the present you. What sacrifices will the you of today be willing make in order to provide for the health, happiness and welfare of that older you of the future?

Module #43
The Second Cornerstone of Focus
is Concentration

"When a man's undivided attention is centered on one object his mind will constantly be suggesting improvements of value, which would escape him if his brain were occupied by a dozen different subjects at once."

P.T. BARNUM

Our goal for this module

To gain an expanded idea of the resources available to any task, and why it is so important to concentrate those resources on the accomplishment of that task.

During World War II, the allies adopted a strategy of "Germany first." This required courage and discipline, since after all it was Japan, and not Germany, that had attacked the U.S. at Pearl Harbor. But President Roosevelt and his generals understood the principle of concentration. By concentrating forces on Europe first, and only after achieving victory there giving priority to the Pacific theater, they were able to sequentially focus military power on their enemies, rather than dispersing it on both fronts simultaneously. As Ralph Waldo Emerson said in the quote under the next heading, concentration is the secret of success in all human affairs, not just in military conflict.

Concentration is the key to success

"Concentration," wrote Ralph Waldo Emerson, *"is the secret of strength in politics, in war, in trade, in short in all management of human affairs."* In the last Module, on the Target Cornerstone of Focus, I covered the importance of clearly defining your goals and priorities. Having done that, the next step is to concentrate all available resources on their achievement. If you can concentrate sufficient energy for a sufficient duration, there is not a mountain that you cannot move, not an impossible dream that you cannot transform into your future reality.

In 1936, during the darkest days of the Great Depression, Dorothea Brand wrote a book entitled *Wake Up and Live!*, which included a chapter on what she called "the will to fail." This was, she said, *"the intention, often unconscious, to fill life so full of secondary activities or substitute activities that there will be no time in which to perform the best work of which one is capable."* If anything, the problem is worse today than it was in 1936, if for no other reason than we have so much more information and so many more choices. You only have so many resources, and how you choose to allocate them will determine the extent of your success (or lack of it) in life.

Pareto Prison (the 80/20 trap)

The Pareto Principle, better known as the 80/20 rule, states that as a general principle 20% of the inputs are responsible for 80% of the results. For example, 20% of the population is responsible for 80% of healthcare costs, and for a typical store 20% of the customers are responsible for 80% of the sales. Put in personal terms, 20% of your activity is responsible for 80% of your results, and the other 80% of your activity generates only 20% of your results.

I call this Pareto Prison, because a failure to concentrate time, energy and other resources on the activities that are most fruitful, more than almost anything else, keeps people from achieving their full potential. As Richard Koch put it in his book *The 80/20 Principle: The Secret to Success by Achieving More With Less*, *"The war is between the trivial many and the vital few."* If you can identify the 20% of your activities that are highly productive and do more of those things, and do less of the 80% that are not as productive, it stands to reason that you will accomplish a great deal more.

> *What one activity, if you were to double the amount of time and energy you devote to it, could increase your results by four times? That is the key with which you can break out of Pareto Prison.*

Outer concentration begins on the inside

Concentration begins as an inside job, which is then manifested in an outside seriousness of purpose and determination of effort. Inner concentration is like the gyroscope that keeps you balanced, stable, and on target. I previously introduced the DDQ, or Direction Deflection Question (*"Will what I'm about to do or say help me be my best self?"*). As I mentioned then, the DDQ is infinitely adaptable, and can be used to help you maintain your inner balance and outer focus. Being clear about your goals (your target), and then asking this DDQ, can help you keep that inner gyroscope balanced and focused:

DIRECTION DEFLECTION QUESTIONS

Is what I am about to do with my time going to help me achieve my most important goals?

Copyright © 2004, Paradox 21 Inc.

It's about time

Napoleon Bonaparte was a master of concentration. Though he was often outnumbered on the overall battlefield, he almost always had the overwhelming force at the decisive point of contact. And he understood that the way to get his forces into position was to move quickly. *"Space,"* he said, *"we can always recover, but time, never."* Procrastination is not only the source of missed opportunity and professional mediocrity (if not outright failure); it is also the cause of much emotional distress. The third and fourth Cornerstones of Focus are Speed and Momentum. One thing that almost all successful people share in common is a real sense of urgency to concentrate their resources, before the opportunity slips away, before the problem gets out of hand, before it's too late.

 ## Rules for the Journey

1) Concentration begins as an inside job, which is then manifested in an outside seriousness of purpose and determination of effort. Inner concentration is like the gyroscope that keeps you balanced, stable, and on target.

---

2) The Pareto Principle (better known as the 80/20 rule) states that as a general principle, 20% of activity is responsible for 80% of results. If you can identify the 20% that's highly productive and do more of that, and do less of the other 80%, you will accomplish a great deal more. To allow 80% of your time to be unproductive is what I call Pareto Prison.

3) To be creative requires the ability to concentrate on one thing, despite all distractions. Meditation exercises can help you train yourself to block out chatter, both internally- and externally-generated, and give your attention to the creative work at hand.

4) Nobody on their deathbed ever will say they wish they'd watched more television. The way to avoid future regrets is to be more aware and judicious when it comes to dribs and drabs of time, and putting them to better use.

5) Just Say No: The more you say "no" to trivia, distractions, temptations, and diversions, the more you will have time, money, and energy to invest in the goals and dreams that are most important.

 ## Take-home exercise: Keep two lists

Keep two lists. The first list is for your "big ticket items," the big dreams and goals you wish to accomplish. The second list is your daily "to-do" list. Every morning before you start your day (or preferably, each evening before you go to bed) review the daily to-do list. Prepare yourself mentally to move quickly and expeditiously through those items that have nothing to do with your "big ticket" goals and dreams, thereby transferring precious minutes from the "urgent" category to be "important" category.

Here's how the two interact. For each item on my to-do list, I ask this question: *"Will the time I spend on this (fill in the blank) materially contribute to the accomplishment of one of the goals that is on my Big Ticket List?"* As you can probably guess, eight out of ten times the answer is *"No."* Simply pausing to ask the question helps me stay more focused. Perhaps I still need to make a phone call that's on my to-do list, even though it's not related to anything on my Big Ticket List—but I know it should be a 45-second call, not a 15-minute call. That email still needs to go out, but since it's not contributing to an important goal, it can be a few sentences rather than a book chapter.

Here's one approach: After you've made out your daily to-do list, go back over it with a highlighter. Highlight only those activities that directly relate to the accomplishment of something that's on your master goals list. Then start your day by doing those things first. Don't move on to secondary stuff (like watching the news or reading email jokes) until the important tasks have been taken care of. This is the best way I know to graduate from *tyranny of the trivial* to *mastery of the important.*

 Extra credit reading

"Writing [a] daily list is one of the smartest things I ever learned to do. I believe in it, heart and soul. Each night, I put together my list for the following day. If I don't get something on my list accomplished, it goes on the next day's list. I put the hardest or most unappealing task at the top of the list. This way, I tackle the most difficult I am first, and once it's out of the way, I feel my day is off to a good start."

MARY KAY ASH: *You Can Have It All: Lifetime Wisdom from America's Foremost Woman Entrepreneur*

Something to think about

Say no to the trivia and say yes to the things that really do matter. You will conquer the tyranny of the trivial and graduate to mastery of the important.

Module #44
The Third Cornerstone of Focus is Speed

"Pursue one great decisive aim with force and determination... It is even better to act quickly and err than to hesitate until the time of action has past."

CARL VON CLAUSEWITZ

Our goal for this module

To understand how moving fast can not only help you stay more focused on what really matters, but also can enhance both the quality and quantity of the results you achieve in your life, and to see just how seriously procrastination and sluggishness can degrade the quality of your life, and understand some of the reasons for these behaviors.

"All things come to one who waits—but they are the things that have been left behind by the ones who hustle." **A friend of mine likes to say this, and whenever he does, I think of the parable of the tortoise and the hare, and how (especially in today's fast-paced world) the hare gets a bad rap. The person who is able to move quickly and decisively (the hare) will almost inevitably accomplish more, and have a more fulfilling life, than the person who plods along (the tortoise). Perhaps that's why the world seems to have a surplus of rabbits while in many places the tortoise is all but extinct!**

The paradox of speed

Speed promotes focus. In the hospital where I started my career, residents in the surgery program had a saying: *See One, Do One, Teach One.* That was not a prescription to be taken literally, but rather an indication that because of the huge knowledge base required to be a surgeon, students must continuously be pushing the envelope in their quest for information and experience. Building a sense of urgency and moving quickly does a great deal to foster focus. When you are moving quickly, there is less chance of being diverted or distracted from your course, and a greater certainty that you will achieve your goal sooner. The paradox of speed is that the faster you move to achieve your goals, the more time you will have for additional goals, and/or for relaxation and rejuvenation.

CAVEAT #1

If you are pursuing inauthentic goals, speed will only get you down the wrong road more quickly, which is why Authenticity is the first Core Action Value.

CAVEAT #2

Speed does not mean sloppiness. As with the urgent quest of the surgical resident for knowledge and skills, speed means moving quickly from one goal to the next, building upon that foundation.

Speed and the learning curve

When I was in business school, we studied "the learning curve." Very briefly, it says that the more you do something (e.g. manufacture a car), the better and the faster you should be able to do it, because you learn as you go. There are significant implications in this for you, in every dimension of your life, whether it's getting ahead in your career, getting out of debt, improving your golf score, or enhancing the quality of your family life. The faster you move, the more quickly you will come down the learning curve. Living a purpose-directed life requires a spirit of intensity. And one the best ways to generate that spirit of intensity is to move fast. *Speed Wills*—willpower increases geometrically when you fire up and put the pedal to the metal.

Speed Wills—Procrastination Kills

Balance urgency and patience

Stephen Covey, famous for his *Seven Habits* program, has made an important contribution with his emphasis on the distinction between urgent and important. We all have urgent matters that must be attended to. The problem arises when we don't give ourselves sufficient time for activities that are important but not necessarily urgent, such as thinking about a personal mission statement, visualizing long term dreams and goals, cultivating stronger relationships with other people, and spending time for reflection and renewal. One of the common characteristics of high achievers is that they have an incredible sense of urgency, coupled with the patience to labor and to wait, because great accomplishments take time. How do they do it? They try a little something, see what works and what doesn't, then try it again. They are not afraid to build a prototype, not afraid to fail. Their sense of urgency is satisfied by constant movement in the direction of the goal, and their patience is rewarded by incremental progress.

There are few shortcuts on the road to success

Moving faster does not necessarily mean taking shortcuts. If, for example, your goal is to become more effective leader, you cannot skip over any of the first eleven Core Action Values—you simply will not be a true leader if you are inauthentic, lack integrity or courage, don't have the capacity to persevere through adversity, don't have a sense of vision and a spirit of purpose, and so forth. You won't get rich without first tending to the details of your personal finances (trust me on this, you are not going to win the lottery), and you won't stay healthy without adequate exercise and proper nutrition. In the same way, over the long term you pay a high price if you try to take a short cut around grief after loss, around introspection after rejection or failure, or around preparation before embarking upon a new venture. We often don't like those intermediate steps, which is why we yearn for shortcuts. But they are essential. There are no shortcuts on the road to success, but in the end you become who you are as a result of the journey, and that makes it all worthwhile.

 ## Rules for the Journey

1) When you're moving quickly, there's less chance of being diverted from your course, and a greater certainty that you will achieve your goal sooner. The faster you achieve your goals, of course, the more time you have for additional goals, and/or for relaxation and rejuvenation.

2) Procrastination is not only the source of missed opportunity and failure; it's also the cause of much emotional distress. Successful people have a sense of

urgency to move quickly, before the opportunity slips away, before the problem gets out of hand, before it's too late.

3) You'll never see a 300-pound jockey win the Kentucky Derby. You move faster if you travel light. Complexity is the enemy of focus, and simplicity is it's ally. The more you can simplify your life, physically and emotionally, the sooner you will achieve the goals that really matter to you.

4) The more willing you are to ask for help, and to delegate to others, the more quickly you will achieve your goals.

5) Moving faster doesn't mean taking shortcuts. Quite to the contrary, skipping essential foundation-building activities in your rush to get to the top will almost inevitably set you up for future failure and unhappiness.

6) To accomplish great things requires the paradoxical blending of a sense of urgency with a spirit of patience. Think big, start small. Start now.

 ## Take-home exercise: Think prototype

A prototype is a working model of something that has yet to be developed. For example, the car in your driveway started life as a prototype in an auto company's design studio. The book on your nightstand (and I do hope that you are currently reading a good book!) might well have started life as a journal article or even a letter to the editor. Getting into the habit of building prototypes can help you move more quickly, because it both reduces risk and encourages action.

But "prototype" can be more than just a physical model—it can also be a state of mind. Any time you find yourself stuck, putting off taking action on an important goal because it seems too big and overwhelming, ask yourself this: *"What is a prototype that I can start to work on right now?"* Whatever it is you want to do, start now by creating a prototype. Your sense of urgency will be satisfied by constant movement in the direction of the goal, and your patience will be rewarded by incremental progress toward the achievement of that goal.

Extra credit reading

"If work expands to fill the available time, the solution is to reduce the amount of time you have to get the work done. When pressed, most people can get the job done in half the time they are currently using... Somehow this turns a dreary task into a fun game. You'll be amazed at how much you can accomplish. Afterward you'll feel great that you've gotten it out of the way, and you'll have more time to do the things you really love."

TALANE MIEDANER: *Coach Yourself to Success*

Something to think about

The more you do, the more you can do. So speed up, and do it now.

Module #45
The Fourth Cornerstone of Focus is Momentum

"Consider the postage stamp. It secures success through its ability to stick to one thing till it gets there."

JOSH BILLINGS

Our goal for this module

To see how Momentum builds upon the three previous cornerstones of Focus (Target, Concentration, and Speed), and in itself is a powerful source of motivation and achievement.

As Dorothy and her companions hurried down the Yellow Brick Road, they were lured into a tempting, but potentially disastrous, diversion—a field full of poppies. From the time Odysseus and his men were tempted to divert from their course by the Sirens, the warning to avoid diversions has been a consistent theme in mythology. Since the greatest human truths are reflected in myths, this is a warning we should all heed—the warning to not become distracted from pursuing the goals and dreams that most matter to us. And paradoxically (as anyone who has ever been on the weight-loss roller-coaster knows) it's easier to maintain forward momentum than it is to start then stop then start again.

Move decisively in the direction of your target

Zig Ziglar is one of the nation's top motivational speakers. One of his secrets of success is to *"move decisively from one task to the next."* In other words, maintain your momentum. This relates to a basic law of physics, that it is easier to keep going than it is to stop and start again. Louis L'Amour wrote over one hundred Western novels during his career. How did he achieve such prodigious productivity? Upon the completion of each novel, after he had typed the words "The End" at the bottom of the last page, before he even got up out of his chair L'Amour scrolled in another piece of paper and typed "Chapter One" at the top of a new page. In this way, he was already anchored in the next book, and thus less likely to slack off, and perhaps never get back to it. The greatest potential gains often don't lie in figuring out how to do tasks more efficiently, but rather in reducing the time wasted between the performance of those tasks. So move decisively from one task to the next.

Momentum = Urgency + Patience

A sense of urgency is needed to overcome inertia and resistance, but it is patience which allows that urgency to be continuously nourished and channeled. Momentum is thus the marriage of urgency plus patience. With this union, you are unstoppable. You become a force of nature—with the urgency of a thunderstorm and the patience of the sea.

> ### *Maintain your momentum by combining the urgency of a thunderstorm with the patience of the sea.*

Momentum is the antidote to entropy

According to the second law of thermodynamics, entropy—the gradual decay from a state of order to a state of disorder—occurs when you stop applying energy to a system. That is true in your life as well (leave a desk full of papers unattended for a while and see what happens!). But it also works in reverse: as you apply energy to a system, you can move from disorder to order. Thinking of your own life as a system, the best way for you to avoid the disorganizing force of entropy is to keep moving—to maintain your momentum.

Momentum is both physical and emotional

We tend to think of momentum as being a physical attribute, as in the progress of a bowling ball headed down an alley toward a row of pins. But it is also emotional. Emotional momentum means working to not allow yourself to be slowed down by anxiety or to be bogged down with negative and depressing thoughts, but rather to maintain your forward emotional momentum with positive thinking and nurturing spiritual inputs. And please note—there is a strong interaction between physical and emotional momentum: if your body is moving forward in a positive and productive way, your emotions will inevitably follow. So keep moving!

Sometimes maintaining momentum means veering to the side

Momentum does not always mean putting your head down and charging straight ahead regardless of the obstacles. As Eric Harvey put it in his book *The Leadership Secrets of Santa Claus*, *"We get things going fast, and then we make mid-course corrections as necessary. And the way we know how we're doing, as well as what adjustments we need to make, is through continual monitoring and measurement."* If you run into a brick wall, you don't maintain momentum by running faster, you maintain momentum by changing direction. Even better, you maintain momentum by anticipating the brick wall before you run into it, by changing direction before you are forced to.

Avoid arrogance and complacence

Over the past ten years or so, dozens of books have been written by athletic coaches about their formula for success. If you read all of these books, you will see many different philosophies concerning motivation, organization, training, etc. The one consistent theme throughout will be this: your greatest success is also the moment of your greatest danger, because that is the point where arrogance and complacence tend to set in. After a victory of some sort, it's human nature to be tempted to step back, pat ourselves on the back, and take it easy for a bit. What great achievers know, however, is that this is precisely the moment to push down harder on the gas pedal. Keeping your momentum is the antidote to arrogance and complacence.

There is no finish line

Track athletes are told to "run through the tape" to prevent them from backing off just short of the finish line. That's good advice for all of us. In my work with individuals and small groups, I often hear people referring to a finish line of some sort—getting the new job or big promotion, the kids going of to school, retirement—as if it were the end of the race. Perhaps the tendency to lose momentum as we approach a perceived finish line of one kind or another accounts for the disappointment and emptiness we sometimes feel. In my book *Your Dreams Are Too Small*, I wrote about "the dream beyond the dream." You should always have a goal, a dream, beyond the next finish line to keep you motivated, to help you maintain your momentum.

Rules for the Journey

1) If you want to be a success, learn to create and sustain momentum. Attack every problem with more force than required, maintain standards higher than expected, and persevere beyond what's reasonable.

2) Momentum = Urgency + Patience. A sense of urgency is needed to overcome inertia and resistance, and patience allows that urgency to be continuously nourished and channeled.

3) Momentum is a key factors in the learning curve. As you get moving, you become more efficient and productive, and the quality of your work goes up. This notion can apply to just about any aspect of your life, from making widgets to parenting and prayer: the more you do it, the better you get.

4) Physical momentum is good for your mental health; stay active.

5) Keep moving—maintaining momentum is the antidote to entropy, complacence and arrogance.

Take-home exercise: Be a racecar

Practice this *Metaphorical Visualization*™ technique: visualize yourself as a racecar plowing through your daily activities like an Indy 500 driver determined to see victory lane, or as a shark who must keep moving in order to stay alive. It's silly, it's fun, and it works!

Extra credit reading

"Momentum is really a leader's best friend. Sometimes it's the only difference between winning and losing... Momentum also makes a huge difference in organizations. When you have no momentum, even the simplest tasks can seem to be insurmountable problems. But when you have momentum on your side, the future looks bright, obstacles appear small, and trouble seems temporary."

JOHN C. MAXWELL: *The 21 Irrefutable Laws of Leadership*

Something to think about

Anyone who has ever allowed themselves to get badly out of shape and then started going to the gym knows that it's much easier to stay in shape than it is to get in shape, and that's a powerful metaphor for the power of momentum in every dimension of life.

The one thing that perhaps more than any other quality that defines people of genius and great accomplishment is their ability to focus on their most important priority, to the exclusion of all else. The more you can say no to the trivial distractions and diversions of today, the more you will say yes to your most cherished goals and dreams of tomorrow.

Core Action Value #10 is Enthusiasm

Ralph Waldo Emerson said "nothing great was ever accomplished without enthusiasm." That applies to organizations, and it also applies to families and to your personal life. By choosing enthusiasm, you will be both happier and more successful.

Cornerstone #1: Attitude

Positive attitudes create can self-fulfilling expectations for success and happiness; negative attitudes more typically create self-fulfilling prophecies of failure and misery.

Cornerstone #2: Energy

Energy is life, and more than many of us will admit, whether or not we have energy in any circumstance is a matter of choice, not physical state.

Cornerstone #3: Curiosity

Enthusiastic people are curious, and their quest for knowledge and understanding helps to fuel their vision for the future.

Cornerstone #4: Humor

It's true that humor is good medicine, but people with a sense of humor are also happier and more successful. Fortunately, you can cultivate a funny bone.

"Enthusiasm has power! When that power is released to support definiteness of purpose and is constantly renewed by faith, it becomes an irresistible power for which poverty and temporary defeat are no match. And it is a power which can be touched off in the mind of another person... Perhaps that is the greatest service anyone can render another, for enthusiasm is a contagious force."

NAPOLEON HILL: *The Science of Success*

Module #46
Core Action Value #10 is Enthusiasm

"Enthusiasm is one of the most powerful engines of success. When you do a thing, do it with your might. Put your whole soul into it. Stamp it with your own personality. Be active, be energetic, be enthusiastic and faithful, and you will accomplish your object. Nothing great was ever achieved without enthusiasm."

RALPH WALDO EMERSON

Our goal for this module

To encourage you to evaluate your own beliefs, attitudes and behaviors and to encourage you to choose to be more passionate, more optimistic, and more cheerful—the essential qualities of the enthusiastic person.

In a previous module I quoted Winston Churchill, who said that success is the ability to move from one failure to the next without loss of enthusiasm. If, as Emerson and Churchill both say, enthusiasm is the magic elixir of success, we should define what we mean by the term. To me, enthusiasm implies three things. First is passion, the ability to be interested in and excited about your work and your life, even when the going is tough. Second is optimism; enthusiastic people expect the best from themselves and others, and work to make good things happen rather than expect bad things to happen. And third, enthusiastic people are cheerful. The good news is that enthusiasm is not a genetic trait, it is a choice and a habit. This magic elixir of success is available to anyone who makes the choice and develops the habit.

The magic elixir of success

Enthusiasm is the spark that creates personal happiness and professional success. Its presence or absence in organizations determines the difference between a negative, high-stress work environment and one that is positive, productive, and resilient. Enthusiasm is more contagious than measles in a daycare center, and it's spreading presence can bring to fruition even the grandest of dreams and most naïve of expectations. Enthusiastic people are happier and more success-ful because they expect to be happier and more successful—they are positive, and they are optimistic. Their enthusiasm becomes the fuel of self empowerment. Enthusiasm is the active ingredient in positive thinking.

Choose to be enthusiastic

There are two essential steps to being enthusiastic. The first step is controlling negative emotions; anxiety and fear, anger and envy, guilt and self-pity are enthu-siasm-killers. Psychologists have demonstrated that the human mind will auto-matically gravitate toward negative, frightening and depressing thoughts unless it is consciously directed in a positive direction. Therefore, consciously cultivating a positive self-image and high self-esteem, and replacing negative self-talk with positive and affirming inner dialog, is the first step to being a more enthusiastic person.

The second step is deliberately stoking positive emotions. If you spend time hang-ing around with negative people who can only complain about how hard life is, or if you while away the hours parked in front of the TV watching bad news and sit-coms, your enthusiasm will evaporate. Conversely, when you spend time speaking with positive people and reading inspiring books, you will inevitably become more enthusiastic yourself.

The happiness revolution

Enthusiasm is directly related to happiness—enthusiastic people tend to be hap-pier than bored and grouchy people. In recent years, happiness researchers (yes, there actually are people who make a living studying the why's and how's of hap-piness) have identified some of the factors that make people happy, or unhappy. Entire books have been written on the subject (see, for example, *Happy for No Reason* by Marci Shimoff and *Stumbling on Happiness* by Daniel Gilbert), but here are the basics.

First, not only will money not buy you happiness, obsessive concern for material things and for "keeping up with the Joneses," is more likely to make you miserable than it is to make you happy. Likewise, it's been shown that comparing yourself (or your salary or status) with others usually results in unhappiness (partly because whenever you make such comparisons, you are comparing yourself at your perceived worst against the other person at their perceived best).

The things that make for happiness, on the other hand, rarely have to do with external circumstances (which is why "winning" the lottery so rarely makes anyone happy for very long). These include such things as gratitude, forgiveness, cheerful optimism, living in the present, and doing work that inspires you. The good news, according to the latest research, is that while about half of what is called your "happiness set-point" is determined by genetics and external circumstances, the other half is determined by your attitude, and choices you make about such things as how you spend your time, how you view events, and how well you cultivate relationships with other people.

 ## Rules for the Journey

1) Make the commitment to enthusiasm by choosing to be passionate, optimistic, and cheerful.

2) Money and material possessions won't buy you happiness, but enthusiasm and a joy for your work and your life will earn it for you.

3) Attitude is contagious. We've all had the experience of having someone walk into a room and suck the energy right out of it with their negativity. We've also had experiences where somebody energized the whole room with the power of a smile. Be an energy faucet, never an energy drain.

4) You tend to get what you expect out of life, so expect the best.

5) Get that pickle out of your mouth by taking *The Pickle Challenge* and *The Pickle Pledge* (keep reading...).

Take-home exercise: Take *The Pickle Challenge* and internalize *The Pickle Pledge*

The Pickle Challenge

I'm fairly certain that wherever you work, your coworkers are not allowed to come into your workspace and foul the air you breathe with the smoke of cigarettes, cigars or pipes. We have eradicated toxic tobacco smoke from the workplace. Toxic emotional negativity is every bit as corrosive to the soul as cigarette smoke is to the body, and in fact much scientific evidence points to the fact that it is also physically harmful. By taking *The Pickle Challenge*, you declare your workspace to be a "pickle-free zone." Hanging a "No Pickle" sign on your door or posting it on the wall of your cubicle alerts the chronic whiners and gossips—people who look like they were born with a dill pickle stuck in their mouths—that they should leave their complaints and their rumors outside, that you don't want your workspace contaminated with their toxic emotional negativity.

The Pickle Pledge

Creating a workplace that is free from toxic emotional negativity begins with you, and the best way for you to begin is to take to heart *The Pickle Pledge*. Read The Pledge, including the footnote, and ask yourself how much happier and more productive you will be if you act upon this promise, and how much more positive and productive your workplace will be if everyone there does the same thing. Then go do it.

**I'VE TAKEN
THE PICKLE PLEDGE™**

"I will turn every complaint into either a blessing or a constructive suggestion."

*By taking The Pickle Pledge, I am promising myself that I will
no longer waste my time and energy on blaming, complaining,
and gossiping, nor will I commiserate with those who steal
my energy with their blaming, complaining, and gossiping.*

Copyright © 2005, Paradox 21 Inc.
800-644-3889

 ## Extra credit reading

"What is it going to be for you: a positive attitude or a negative attitude? The choice seems fairly simple, doesn't it? The problem is that we often forget we have a choice. That is one of the master keys to unlocking your greatness in life—exercising your power to choose your attitude and your approach to life's challenges... You should choose your attitude thoughtfully because it determines how you respond to the many challenges you will encounter."

KEITH HARRELL: *Attitude is Everything:
10 Life-Changing Steps to Turning Attitude into Action*

Something to think about

"Every negative thought must be set aside before it takes root."

I CHING

Module #47
The First Cornerstone of Enthusiasm is Attitude

"I've learned from experience that the greater part of our happiness or misery depends on our dispositions and not our circumstances. We carry the seeds of the one or the other about with us in our minds wherever we go."

MARTHA WASHINGTON

Our goal for this module

To make the commitment to avoid negative attitudes and cultivate positive attitudes ourselves, and then spreading this positivity where we work and live.

A little boy is out in his backyard with a baseball and a bat. *"At the bottom of the ninth, the greatest batter in the world has just come to the plate,"* **he says in his best imitation of a radio announcer's voice. He tosses the ball in the air and takes a mighty swing— and misses.** *"Strike one,"* **announces the boy. He tosses the ball into the air once more, takes another mighty swing—and again misses.** *"Strike two,"* **he exclaims,** *"and the crowd is on its feet."* **With a look of determined intensity, he tosses the ball into the air a third time, takes another mighty swing— and misses for the third time. For just one second, the little boy looks dejected, then he smiles, pumps his fist in the air and shouts into his make-believe microphone,** *"Oh my, sports fans! Can you believe it? The greatest batter in the world has just been struck out by the world's greatest pitcher!"*

Attitude is everything

Attitude really is everything (for more on this, see books of the same title by Jeff Keller, Keith Harrell and others). Is ours the best of times or the worst of times? Is the world a place of scarcity and risk, or a place of abundance and opportunity?

Can you influence your own destiny, or is your future out of your control, in the hands of others? Are you grateful for the blessings of your life, or are you resentful about what you don't have? How you answer these questions is substantially defined by your attitude. And because people tend to get what they expect out of life, a positive attitude is one of your most important assets for creating a future filled with blessings and abundance.

Your attitude will determine your altitude!

Don't Catch Dilbert Disease

If you read the comic strip *Dilbert*, you know that the "hero" of this strip hates his job, can't stand his boss, and despises the morons he has to work with. You also know that his biggest fear is losing his job. That's a neurotic condition I refer to as Dilbert Disease. You probably know people who are suffering from this condition, and you may, on occasion, experience these symptoms yourself. Beware! Dilbert Disease is contagious and it is malignant. People with Dilbert Disease are low-energy low-performers, and their negativity rubs off on those they spend time with. In his beautiful book *The Prophet*, Kahlil Gibran said that work "is love made visible." One of the surest ways to create a great future for yourself is to put love and enthusiasm into your work, and to stay far away from people who have Dilbert Disease.

Be positive when it really counts

It's easy to have a positive attitude when the sun is shining, you've just gotten a pay raise, and you're about to go on vacation. It's much more difficult, but far more important, to maintain that positive attitude when things aren't going well. So how can you make sure that you maintain a positive attitude when you run into those inevitable obstacles and setbacks? The single-most important action you can take is to prepare yourself before trouble strikes by reading books and listening to audio programs that inspire you (even if they don't entertain you); cultivating relationships with positive people and avoiding the company of negative people; and making the commitment to yourself that when you run into those speed bumps, you will remain passionate, optimistic, and cheerful. This might mean that you have to take that most famous advice from AA—fake it 'til you make it.

"Successful people expect to face hurdles. They know that overcoming obstacles is a normal part of life, and they plan accordingly. They face their challenges instead of fearing them."

JOHN C. MAXWELL: *The Difference Maker:*
Making Your Attitude Your Greatest Asset

What attitude will not do for you

A positive attitude will not make you a trial lawyer or a brain surgeon. Only many years of study and hard work will do that. But your attitude *will* profoundly influence your willingness to begin that work, the quality of your effort in doing the work, and what you do with it once you've finished.

Know when to change your reference group

Sociologists tell us that one of the most important, if not *the* most important influence on our lives is the people we spend time with, the people with whom we identify. It's what they call our "reference group." We are all profoundly imprinted by the characteristics of the reference groups with which we identify, in both conscious and subconscious ways. If your reference group consists primarily of people who are depressed, pessimistic, and chronically whining about how the world is victimizing them, over time it will be almost impossible for you to not fall into that emotional quicksand. On the other hand, if you are depressed and anxious yourself but spend time with people who are confident and optimistic, their attitudes will begin to rub off on you.

One of the surest ways to begin changing your life for the better is to change—or expand—your reference group. You do this by consciously seeking out people who have the qualities you admire, and that you would like to emulate. This entails sticking your neck out, making those proverbial cold calls, joining Rotary or the Optimists Club, and otherwise getting out of your shell. The payback can be enormous, both personally and professionally.

Rules for the Journey

1) There is no "attitude gene" determining whether you are going to be positive or negative, optimistic or pessimistic. It is a choice you make, many times each day.

2) One of the most important, and often overlooked, determinants of productivity (not to mention morale) within any organization is the collective attitude of the people who work there. When people are focused on that which is positive and constructive, morale and productivity are enhanced.

3) Program your mental computer for positivity; erase and rewrite negative self-talk; avoid toxic emotional negativity (as reflected in criticizing, complaining, finger-pointing, and gossiping); get your body into the act; and inoculate yourself against Dilbert Disease.

4) Any time you catch yourself whining about something, turn it into a blessing instead, as in: *"My back is killing me... Thank God for ibuprofen."*

5) Turn every complaint into a call to action, then do it or drop it, but don't dwell on it. The best way to do this is to make *The Pickle Pledge* part of your life.

 Take-home exercise: Cultivate a support group environment where you work

There's nothing you can do that can't be done... there's no one you can save that can't be saved... all you need is love.

THE BEATLES

Whenever I have the chance, I like to visit with support groups. I've seen amazing, even miraculous, things occur as people share their stories. At their best, support groups help people find courage, strength, and awareness to take responsibility for their health and take charge of their lives, and to not allow themselves to become self-perceived victims of unfortunate circumstances. Whether people are gathered to help each other conquer addictions, cope with cancer, or console each other for loss, the environment is almost always compassionate, respectful, and collegial. I've often thought that any organization which could capture this "support group" sense of shared experience and mutual support would become unstoppable. They would be much more competitive at recruiting good people, and those people would be much less likely to leave. Here are some of the principles I've observed at work in support groups.

Principle #1: Confidentiality

What is shared in a support group meeting stays with the group and does not become grist for the rumor mill. Imagine how much more positive and productive a workplace would be where gossip was treated as the shameful and unethical invasion of another soul's sacred space that it really is.

Principle #2: Optimism

In a support group, people don't share their stories to complain and seek pity—everyone else in the room is facing the same or greater problems. They share their stories as a way of giving each other hope. Imagine a workplace where people always looked for the hidden blessing in every adversity and expected the best outcome from every situation, which is what you see in a support group.

Principle #3: Acceptance

A key role of the support group is helping people accept the reality of their situations, which is often the first step in letting go and moving on. Imagine a workplace where, instead of wasting energy whining about things that cannot be changed, people focused that energy to work on the things that can be changed.

Principle #4: Non-judgment

At an AA meeting, it doesn't matter if you're Joe the janitor or Joe the CEO; for that hour, you're just Joe the alcoholic. Imagine a workplace where people didn't just talk about how everyone is equally important to the organization, they acted like they really meant it.

Principle #5: Uplifting

With very few exceptions, I've never seen anyone leave a support group meeting who was not somehow better off for the experience, whether it's the cancer patient who's been given a shot of hope or the drug addict who's been confronted with the consequences of his denial. Imagine a workplace where our collective commitment was that, while we might leave physically exhausted and mentally drained at the end of our day, we would also go home having been spiritually uplifted.

Imagine a workplace that had the characteristics of a support group. I'll bet your first thought would be that you'd like to work there, and your second would be that such an organization is destined for greatness. If that's the case, then your third thought should be, *"What can I personally do to help bring about this transformation where I work?"* Here's the good news: You don't need permission from the CEO, you don't need an outside consultant, and you don't need a big budget to make it happen. All you need is the support of your coworkers, including your immediate manager. And here are two simple things you can do to get started. First, call a staff meeting and share these five principles—ask your coworkers to make the commitment to live them on the work unit. Second, go to the Pledge Power website (www. Pledge-Power.com) and print out copies of *These Self-Empowerment Pledge*, then ask your coworkers to take the appropriate promise to heart each day of the week.

 Extra credit reading

"An evangelistic leader believes that the cause will succeed and then sets an inspiring example by withstanding long and difficult battles, fostering collaborative efforts, showing composure in difficult times, and remaining humble in victory. He plants his feet firmly on the ground yet keeps his dreams in the clouds."

GUY KAWASAKI: *Selling the Dream*

Something to think about

"The longer I live, the more I realize the impact of attitude on life. Attitude, to me, is more important than facts. It is more important than the past, than education, than money, than circumstances, than failures, than successes, than what other people think or say or do. It is more important than appearance, giftedness, or skill. The remarkable thing is we have a choice every day regarding the attitude we will embrace for that day... I am convinced that life is 10% what happens to me, and 90% how I react to it."

CHARLES SWINDOLL

Module #48
The Second Cornerstone of Enthusiasm is Energy

"Enthusiasm is the electricity of life. How do you get it? You act enthusiastic until you make it a habit."

GORDON PARKS

Our goal for this module

To realize that the choices we make substantially determine how energized our lives will be, and to make the commitment that we will make the right choices.

Are you an energy faucet or an energy drain? An energy faucet is the person who walks into a room and with a smile, a kind word, and a positive, enthusiastic attitude. An energy drain is the person who walks into a room and sucks the energy right out of the atmosphere with a frown, with critical, cynical, and pessimistic comments, and with a negative attitude. The energy faucet comes into the room bearing a beautiful gift. The energy drain is a thief who steals from people their most precious resource—their life energy. Make the commitment to be an energy faucet and to never, ever be an energy drain.

Enthusiasm takes energy, and energy is a choice

When people tell me they don't have enough time, money, love or anything else in their lives, it doesn't take long before we come to the conclusion that the missing ingredient is really energy. If they had more energy, they would do the things they have to do in order to create more money, more time, more love, more of whatever they're missing. And that energy is a choice. The fatigue that holds us back is usually more emotional than it is physical. If you don't believe this, imagine yourself at your most exhausted. Then imagine the phone ringing and being told that you'd just inherited a million dollars, or that there's been an accident and you need to go to the hospital immediately. You would suddenly be infused with a burst of energy, wouldn't you? Where did that energy come from? The energy was always there; you were just waiting for some outside factor to motivate you to tap into that energy. The technical scientific term for this phenomenon of pretending to not have energy is—LAZY!

Energy is the resource that renews itself

Imagine coming home from work after one of *those* days. You are frazzled, frustrated and exhausted. All you really want to do is go plop down on the sofa with comfort food and your favorite beverage and turn on the boob tube. But somehow you tap into that last fading reserve of inner energy and force yourself to do something physical: you go for a walk, ride the exercise bike, put on loud rowdy music and do jumping jacks. Question: after using this last fragment of energy, do you have more or less in your tank? Almost without exception, the answer will be more. Personal energy is the ultimately renewable resource—the more you use it, the more you will have of it.

Get enough sleep

Sleep deprivation can increase anxiety and worry, says James Mass in his book *Power Sleep.* When you skimp on sleep, he says you can end up with *"overwhelming feelings of not being able to cope, even with simple problems or moderate work loads; increase in worry, frustration, and nervousness; and inability to maintain perspective, or to relax, even under moderate pressure."* Most of us require *at least* eight (8!!!!) full hours of sleep every night. *"The process of sleep,"* he says, *"if given adequate time and the proper environment, provides tremendous power. It restores, rejuvenates, and energizes the body and the brain."* Turning off the TV and setting aside that murder mystery novel so you can go to bed earlier will help you be more fully alert, creative, enthusiastic, and alive during your waking hours.

Master the fine art of strategic laziness

Imagine trying to pound a nail into a piece of wood by pushing on it with a hammer. It will go a lot faster if you bring the hammer back to a resting position then swing it down hard onto the nail. That's an apt metaphor for strategic laziness. We all need quiet time, time alone for reflection and introspection. Sometimes the most productive thing you can do is stop working on the urgent demands that always seem to be at hand, and take some time to think about the important matters that can profoundly change the direction of your life.

 ## Rules for the Journey

1) Enthusiasm requires energy; you can have more of the energy you need by taking care of yourself (e.g. diet, exercise, getting enough sleep), but you also need to acknowledge that you *always* have energy—the real question is whether you can bring yourself to tap into it. To a greater extent than many of us care to admit to ourselves, whether or not we have the energy to do the things we want to do and the things we must do is based on a decision made at a point of apparent fatigue.

2) Any time someone brings a coworker down with their toxic emotional negativity, they are stealing something far more precious than money; they are stealing energy. For the organization, energy is productivity; for the human being, energy is life.

3) Take care of yourself by getting enough sleep (most of us require 8 hours a night), by eating a reasonably balanced diet and avoiding empty calories, getting some exercise every day, and drinking more water and less soda.

4) Stress and fatigue are caused by inactivity, not by hard work. Do your work with passion; you'll be astonished at how much energy you have.

5) The amazing paradox of energy: you create energy by using it.

Take-home exercise: Get your body into the act

People who have a positive and strong self image tend to have more energy than those who don't like what they see when they look in the mirror. In their book *Mental Toughness*, Dr. James E. Loehr and Peter J. McLaughlin say that *"improving self-image is the key to successful coaching in every sport; the players will be as good as they believe they are...Your self-image is the most important tool in your mental arsenal; it controls your emotions when a challenge appears. If you see yourself as someone who can surmount the challenge, you will."* Cultivating a more positive self-image can be a powerfully effective way to increase your energy. *You will not for long exceed the capacity of the person you see when you look in the mirror.* So make sure that you don't pretend to see less than what is really there!

One of the best ways to develop that strong self-image is to get your body into the act. There is now incredible scientific research documenting the complex interactions between body, mind, and spirit, and between rational thinking and emotional feeling. When you stand straight and tall, walk faster, put a big smile on your face, and act "as if" you had all the confidence in the world, you begin to believe it. And the more you believe it, the less of an act it becomes.

Extra credit reading

"Passion generates a supply of positive energy far more abundant than vitamins, exercise, or any other health remedy you can imagine. When you're passionate about what you do, it's not just the destination that matters, but the entire journey. From beginning to end, the journey is an adventure. When you love what you do, you have the energy to overcome any obstacle."

CYNTHIA KERSEY: *Unstoppable*

Something to think about

If you're unhappy, chances are all that stands between you and happiness is an expenditure of energy—emotional and physical.

Module #49
The Third Cornerstone of Enthusiasm is Curiosity

"Twenty years from now you will be more disappointed by the things that you didn't do than by the ones you did do. So throw off the bowlines. Sail away from the safe harbor. Catch the trade winds in your sails. Explore. Dream. Discover."

MARK TWAIN

Our goal for this module

To respark the childlike (not childish) spirit of curiosity that inspires us to want to know how the world works, and how we might make it work even better.

Is anyone more enthusiastic than a two-year old? The little tykes are always asking: *"Why?"* Like Kipling's Elephant's Child from the classic children's story, toddlers are blessed with insatiable curiosity. We humans are the curious species. We're the only creatures who ask questions, who wonder why birds fly, why the sky is blue and why the grass is green. One of the surest ways for you to re-spark your own spirit of enthusiasm is to start asking better questions. Replace *"Why me?"* with *"Why is the sky blue?"* You'll learn a lot more, you'll earn a lot more, and you'll be a lot happier to boot.

Enthusiasm and creativity feed on one another

What comes first: enthusiasm or creativity? This mirrors one of the oldest debates in the field of human behavior: what comes first, changes in attitude or changes in behavior? The answer is, it doesn't matter! You can think your way into new ways of behaving, or you can act your way into new attitudes, and the most successful approach is to do both simultaneously. Likewise, by becoming more enthusiastic you will become more curious, and by asking better questions you will become more enthusiastic. The key is to start, and having started, to not stop. And one of the secrets to being more creative is to...

Ask dumb questions

Some of the greatest inventions, intellectual breakthroughs, and business innovations in history have come when someone asked how, why, or why not about something that everyone else considered to be self-evident, and came up with a surprisingly new answer. Velcro, the Pet Rock, sliced bread, the theory of relativity, open book management—the list of discoveries and innovations that began with someone challenging conventional wisdom is endless. In our culture we do not place a premium on looking dumb. To the contrary, we honor and reward intelligence and knowledge. People who think they already know the answers rarely ask dumb questions. But it is precisely the people who ask questions that other people think are "dumb" who end up making the greatest creative breakthroughs.

Destroy judgment and create curiosity

As I look back on my career as a student, one of the most influential classes I ever took was Michael Ray's famous "Creativity in Business" course at the Stanford Graduate School of Business. Since graduating in 1985, my career has followed a very non-traditional path (to say the least). Professor Ray's course helped me learn how to think outside of the box, which was the prerequisite for working outside of that box. One of the most important things I learned was to identify what Michael cals the Voice of Judgment (VoJ). VoJ can deaden your creativity. As he notes in his book *Creativity in Business*, one of the best defenses is to replace judgment with curiosity. In his *Letters to a Young Poet*, the German poet Rainer Maria Rilke said that to be creative, one had to train one's doubt. When doubt says *"it will never work,"* train it by forcing it to ask more curious, and constructive, questions, like this: *"what must I do to make this magnificent dream become my future reality?"*

Train Your Doubt!

Trust your intuition

Professor Ray also collaborated on *The Creative Spirit,* which was the companion book to the PBS special. The thing that most impressed me with the creative people who were featured in that book is that they had to overcome the same fears and doubts that you and I have. The major difference, in many cases, between the creative and non-creative person is simply that the creative person had the courage to trust his or her own intuition. The authors say: *"We often underestimate the power of the unconscious mind. But it is far more suited to a creative insight than is the conscious mind. There are no self-censoring judgments in the unconscious, where ideas are free to recombine with other ideas in novel patterns and unpredictable associations in a kind of promiscuous fluidity."*

Fear is the great curiosity killer

Fear can be a serious learning disability when it prevents us from getting outside of our comfort zone, from asking questions (even dumb questions), and from learning from experience. Fear is a curiosity killer. On the other hand, one of the surest ways to overcome fear is to become more curious, to ask more and better questions. As Richard Farson and Ralph Keyes say in their book *Whoever Makes the Most Mistakes Wins: The Paradox of Innovation,* "Nothing undermines innovation more effectively than fear. By the same token, nothing encourages innovation better than finding ways to cope with fear. Real innovation is most likely to take place among those who aren't hamstrung by anxiety."

 ## Rules for the Journey

1) Boredom is a major risk factor that not only results in an unfulfilling life, but also fosters depression; it can even cause serious and potentially fatal diseases, including heart disease. Curiosity is a great antidote.

2) Fear is a serious learning disability when it stops us from getting out of our comfort zones, from asking questions (especially "dumb" questions), and learning from experience. One of the surest ways to overcome fear is to be more curious, to ask more and better questions.

3) Zen wisdom: In the expert's mind there are few possibilities (because the expert thinks he knows everything); in the beginner's mind the possibilities are endless. Be a beginner—be curious—be a questioner.

4) The only dumb question is the one that's not asked.

5) One of the most effective ways you can keep your edge is to make a regular practice of going off on journeys—to the library, to professional meetings, to the distant reaches of your organization, to the Grand Canyon. The journey itself is less important than your state of mind in making it. Take a journal, take a camera, and take your native inquisitiveness.

 ### Take-home exercise: Play the game of news reporter

One way to become a better and more curious listener is to imagine that you are a news reporter who will have to write an account of each conversation. To help you maintain your objectivity, periodically imagine yourself floating above the room looking down on the scene—watching yourself as if you are another person. You can enhance your skills by watching skilled interviewers and the way they use questions to elicit information and opinions from the people they are interviewing.

 ### Extra credit reading

"Without a burning curiosity, a lively interest, we are unlikely to persevere long enough to make a significant new contribution. This kind of interest is rarely only intellectual in nature. It is usually rooted in deep feelings, in memorable experiences that need some sort of resolution—a resolution that can be achieved only by a new artistic expression or a new way of understanding. Someone who is motivated solely by the desire to become rich and famous might struggle hard to get ahead but will rarely have enough inducement to work beyond what is necessary, to venture beyond what is already known."

MIHALY CSIKSZENTMIHALYI: *Creativity: Flow and the Psychology of Discovery and Invention*

Something to think about

If you don't have a question, you don't have a clue; if you aren't searching, you are truly lost.

MCZEN

Module #50
The Fourth Cornerstone of Enthusiasm is Humor

"A person without a sense of humor is like a wagon without springs, jolted by every pebble in the road."

HENRY WARD BEECHER

Our goal for this module

To appreciate the value of humor in so many different dimensions of life: health and happiness; sales, career, and leadership effectiveness; and emotional equanimity and spiritual peace.

Many years ago, I was working in a large organization and had some significant differences of opinion with another executive. As sort of a peace offering, I sent him a book I'd read and enjoyed entitled *Small Decencies*. Upon opening the package, he took a quick look at the cover and thought the title was *Small Deficiencies*. Jumping to the conclusion that this was my way of taking a jab at him, he set it aside. Fortunately, later on he took a closer look, and not only liked the book himself, he got copies for members of his team. Today we're both taking new paths in life, and not only are we good friends, but we've worked together (and continue to work together) in a variety of capacities. The turning point in our relationship was probably the day we shared a laugh over "that small deficiencies book." Humor is not only the best medicine, it's often the best management.

Lighten up

In a 1995 survey of top executives by Accountemps, it was found that 90% said a good sense of humor is important for anyone desiring to reach senior management. George Valliant, a Harvard University psychologist, followed a group of Harvard graduates for over three decades. He found that those with a better sense of humor, which he measured by assigning a value for *HQ* (humor quotient), were both healthier and wealthier, and more likely to be promoted, than their humor-challenged compatriots.

C.W. Metcalf, author of *Lighten Up!*, talks about the problem of "terminal professionalism" in our organizations. He's right. We do need to lighten up, we do need to bring fun back into the workplace, and we do need to laugh at our little boo-boos instead of agonizing over them. Not only is it good for your health, it's good for your career. Oh, by the way, it's also good for your soul. No matter what profession or occupation you have (or aspire to), one of the best investments you can make in yourself might well be to cultivate your funny bone.

Humor and the art of overcoming procrastination

One of the reasons people procrastinate is the fear that whatever it is they're supposed to be doing won't be done right, and they will look foolish if they even try. In *Whoever Makes the Most Mistakes Wins* (which I quoted above), Richard Farson says that fear of embarrassment is the most debilitating fear of all. One of the most effective ways I've discovered for overcoming procrastination caused by my own fear of embarrassment is prospectively knowing that I can laugh at myself. I imagine myself screwing up so badly that everyone else in the world is laughing at me—then I visualize myself joining in on the laughter. And then I realize that not only could I survive whatever *faux pas* I had committed, if I maintained my sense of humor I'd actually learn from it, and perhaps make some new friends along the way. When you're willing to laugh at yourself, it removes one of the most serious obstacles to your own progress, and one of the greatest causes of procrastination—your fear of embarrassment.

Humor is the ultimate emotional muscle

I was recently on an airplane waiting for the delayed take-off of our flight. I was seated several rows from a 30-ish looking guy who was quite obviously a weight-lifter. He had the shoulders of a buffalo, barely covered with a skimpy tank-top that had a set of bent barbells imprinted on the back. Physically, he was an imposing sight. As we sat there stone-still on the tarmac, "Hercules" pulled out his cell phone and made a call, and gave an earful to whoever was listening on the other side. It seemed that the entire world had conspired to victimize this poor baby from the moment he got up on the wrong side of bed—the breakfast waitress who didn't bring coffee fast enough, the airline employees who made him wait in line, the stupid air traffic controllers who were keeping us on the ground. On and on he went.

Here was a guy who was strong on the outside, but weak on the inside. He'd clearly spent many hours developing muscles that mean a great deal when you're in high school, but had never developed the emotional muscles that most make a difference in the adult world of real life. Paramount among those muscles is the ability to maintain a sense of humor, to laugh off the little complaints and challenges, and keep a positive perspective even when the rest of the world doesn't drop everything to wait on you with fresh hot coffee.

> *"Humor is a powerful analgesic. It's free, non-prescription, has no side effects, and is completely habit-forming."*
>
> ROGER CRAWFORD: *How High Can You Bounce?*

Send in the clowns

When Norman Cousins was told by his doctors that his disease was terminal and there was nothing more that they could do for him, he came up with his own prescription—he devoted his days to reading books and watching movies that made him laugh, and he avoided all sources of negativity. The doctors proclaimed it a medical miracle, but we know today that his classic book *Anatomy of an Illness* was the brilliant intuitive leap of a layperson who anticipated future developments in the field of psychoneuroimmunology (the study of body, mind, spirit interrelationships). It is now absolutely clear that humor and laughter are important to health and healing.

It's not humor if it makes someone else feel bad

If you watch what passes for comedy on television, you will quickly notice that much of the so-called humor is at somebody else's expense. Maybe that's why all of the laughter you hear on sitcoms comes from cans. Humor that makes somebody else feel bad, including sexist or racist humor, is not really humor. And just because somebody appears to be laughing and going along with it doesn't mean they're enjoying it. Sarcastic humor, gallows humor, and humor that is at the expense of others will eventually poison your outlook on life and hurt your career.

 ## Rules for the Journey

1) Appreciate the value of humor in so many different dimensions of life: health and happiness; sales, career, and leadership effectiveness; and emotional equanimity and spiritual peace. Having a good sense of humor, a strong funny bone, can help you be more successful in your work.

2) Make yourself laugh. Read the funnies, go to the joke sections in *Readers Digest*, get the complete collection of *Calvin & Hobbes* cartoons, take a child to the zoo, read *A Walk in the Woods* by Bill Bryson. People like to hang around with other people who make them laugh; people who laugh a lot live longer and live happier. What's to lose—other than the Pickle?

3) It's not humor if it puts someone down.

4) What is one thing you can (and will) do to bring more fun, joy, and humor into your workplace?

 ## Take-home exercise: Create a Joy List

In his seminars, C.W. Metcalf tells his listeners to create a Joy List, a roster of the things that bring them joy. The first time you try this, he says, your experience is likely to be similar to his the first time out. When he first created a joy list, he said, it would have been easier for him to make up a list of things that made him grumpy. Here's what he had to say in his book *Lighten Up* about his experience in asking audiences to create a joy list: *"I was surprised to find...most people over thirty could not come up with more than a half-dozen items. Evidently, I wasn't the only human being who had bought into the idea that realistic, professional, and adult meant serious, uptight, and grouchy."*

Try it yourself. Create your own joy list. Sit down with an pad of paper and a pen and start writing down all the things that bring you joy, all the things that make you laugh. Keep going until you get stuck. When the joys start coming to you in a trickle instead of a torrent, bring someone else into the game—a spouse, a friend, or a trusted coworker. Go back and forth like it's a badmitton game, with each person asking the other *"What brings you joy?"* and then scribbling down the word as you volley the question back over the net. Don't throw the list away when you're done. Put it somewhere that you'll see it fairly often, and when you do, pull it out and add something new.

Oh, by the way, Metcalf has lived with "terminal" cancer for nearly a decade. While he might not tell us that his light-hearted approach to life is responsible, he probably would say that it's been much more fun than being "serious, uptight and grouchy" would have been.

 Extra credit reading

"One of the best ways of dealing with worry, or any stress in life, is to use humor. Make friends with amusing people. Laugh as much as you can. Keep in mind that it's OK to laugh, even when times are tough. Make jokes out of bad times. Not only is it OK, it's an excellent idea. Toxic worry almost always entails a loss of perspective; humor almost always restores it."

EDWARD M. HALLOWELL, M.D.: *Worry:*
Controlling it and Using It Wisely

Something to think about

Remember: Nobody ever <u>really</u> died laughing!

Without enthusiasm even play is a chore; with enthusiasm even work is fun.

Core Action Value #11 is Service

Whatever you most need in life, the best way for you to get it is to help someone else get it who needs it even more than you do.

Cornerstone #1: Helpfulness

It's important that you reach out to help others, but even more important is the spirit in which you provide that help.

Cornerstone #2: Charity

It is a good thing to donate money to worthwhile causes, and even better to donate your time and energy.

Cornerstone #3: Compassion

Look beneath external appearances and circumstances to perceive the reality of the human being beneath those superficialities.

Cornerstone #4: Renewal

Take care of yourself and ask for help when you need it, because you cannot pour out of an empty pitcher.

> *"Each of us will define and measure success differently. Some will place more emphasis on the economic score-card than others. No matter what your choice, if you are to succeed, you must understand that your rewards in life will be in direct proportion to the contribution you make."*

DAVID MCNALLY: *Even Eagles Need a Push*

Module #51
Core Action Value #11 is Service

"There is no higher religion than human service. To work for the common good is the greatest creed."

ALBERT SCHWEITZER

Our goal for this module

To appreciate that service is not just something you do, it's a state of mind, and that when one person serves another, two people end up being served.

This is the oldest paradox in the history of the world: if you want to be successful, the best way is to help someone else be successful; if you want to be happy, the best way is to help someone else be happy. This lesson is portrayed in the movie *Mr. Holland's Opus*. Glenn Holland is an aspiring young composer who, in order to support his family, takes a job as a high school music teacher. This, he imagines, will give him plenty of free time to compose. Only it doesn't quite work out that way. Inexorably, he finds himself being pulled into student mentoring, marching band practices, and school musicals, with less and less time for composing.

During a career spanning 30 years, Mr. Holland teaches thousands of students about music appreciation, and profoundly touches the lives of several of them. But at the end of the movie, an administrative decision is made to cut the school's music department. Mr. Holland is now out of a job. Having cleaned out his desk, he makes his way toward the door for the last time. But on the way out, he hears a commotion in the auditorium. It sounds like singing! It turns out to be a surprise farewell party, the highlight of which is a full orchestra comprised of his former students playing the world premier of his own composition, American Symphony. Mr. Holland is invited to conduct. With that, the movie ends.

But the end of the movie never means the end of the story, does it? I imagine a sequel—*Mr. Holland's Encore*—in which some of the students he so lovingly taught now help to promote his work; he at last becomes the famous composer he has always dreamed of being. Had Mr. Holland achieved fame and fortune earlier in life, he might have ended up superficial shell of a man, too puffed up with his own importance to care much about the lives of others. But as we watch his hair turn from brown to gray and his walk go from a quick trot to a slow shuffle, another transformation is visible: Mr. Holland is becoming authentic. The real Mr. Holland is first and foremost a teacher and a mentor who cares deeply about his students. The fame and fortune he achieves as a composer in my imagined encore is simply the unanticipated payback for a lifetime of service to his students.

Service as a value, not just an activity

We've all heard the word "service" a lot in recent years. We know that ours has become a service economy, and that a majority of us have become service workers. We know that excellent customer service is critical to the long term success and survival of our organizations, and with it our own job security and opportunities for enhancement and advancement. And while it is an ancient concept, the idea of servant leadership—that those who would lead must first be committed to be servants for those who follow them—is an idea that has gained considerable currency in recent years. Service becomes *a value*, and not just a series of activities, when it is engrained as an underlying philosophy which informs attitudes and guides actions.

The paradox of service

Service begins with a sincere desire to help other people, which is then followed up by action. It is an ancient paradox that he person who gives a helping hand often benefits as much or more than the person being helped. Zig Ziglar has written many books on motivation and success, and each of them contains this sentence: *"You can have everything in life you want if you will just help enough other people get what they want."*

The 3-Ws of serving

I was once recruiting members for a nonprofit board, and someone gave me the advice to seek out people who could offer one or more of the 3-Ws—wealth, work, and wisdom. The easiest to get, he told me, was wealth, but the other two are much more valuable. You might not think that you have wealth to give, but you do have wisdom and you do have the capacity to work. Think of a way that you can share your wisdom and your work, then pick up the phone and make a call offering to be of service.

Don't wait to be asked

Many years ago, I was chief operating officer for a large community teaching hospital. One year, a member of the Housekeeping Department came in the day before Christmas bringing exquisitely wrapped presents for every child in the pediatrics unit. No one asked her to do it—and she had saved the money from her own paycheck. The following year, everyone in her department brought gifts, and the year after that it become a hospital-wide phenomenon. That was a great example of servant leadership in action, since a leader by definition is someone who has followers. Here's another definition: a leader is a person who takes you to a place you didn't know you wanted to go. That housekeeper had a vision of service that had not occurred to any of the rest of us, and we followed her example. That is what servant leaders do.

Rules for the Journey

1) Service begins with a sincere desire to help others, which is then followed up by action. It's an ancient paradox that he person who gives a helping hand often benefits as much or more than the person being helped.

2) Whether it is in giving wealth, wisdom or work, there is always a way that each of us can be of service to others.

3) Service lies at the heart of servant leadership.

Take-home exercise: Go on a reverse scavenger hunt

Go on a reverse scavenger hunt. Seek out a simple opportunity to perform a small random act of kindness. For example, complement someone on what a great job they're doing or how nice they look; find someone who looks like a lost soul and start a conversation in which you mostly just listen; slip a dollar bill under the windshield wiper of an anonymous car in the parking lot. Think about how it felt to offer to help someone, perhaps someone that would never even know who performed the service. Now think about how an outbreak of random acts of kindness could help create a more friendly and service-oriented organization in the place that you work.

Extra credit reading

"At some point each of us has to discover that our self-interest is better served by doing good work than getting good things. The more our job and our survival is on the line, the easier it is to make this discovery. In this way hard times are an ally."

PETER BLOCK: *Stewardship: Choosing Service Over Self-Interest*

Something to think about

"Here is a test to find whether your mission on earth is finished: If you're alive, it isn't."

RICHARD BACH: *ILLUSIONS*

Module #52
The First Cornerstone of Service is Helpfulness

"It is one of the great secrets of life that those things which are most worth doing, we do for others."

LEWIS CARROLL

Our goal for this module

To understand a commitment to helping others as the foundation of a service mindset, and also to internalize the fact that helping others is often the best way of helping ourselves in the ways that most matter.

Years ago, at a time when I was "between jobs," I volunteered at a shelter for homeless people who had AIDS. Back then, the diagnosis was a virtually certain death sentence. The shelter was ruled with a velvet touch by a woman I'll call Carol. She was infected with the HIV virus when she injected herself with heroin using a contaminated needle. I asked her a question that I've asked many people since (the answer is almost always the same): if she could go back and undo the needle stick, be free of AIDS, but the price would be that she'd be the person she would have been had it never happened, would she do it?

Carol did not hesitate for a moment. *"No way,"* she said. *"I'd love to know that I was going to live for a long time, but I would not trade another 50 years of being Carol the Party Girl for five minutes of the person I am today. I used to just have drinking buddies,"* she said, *"but now I know what it is to have real friends."* She went on to speak about how it was only through helping others that she finally began to find herself.

The high road to success

A great real world example of helpfulness is Ray Kroc, who at the age of 54 began the process of transforming one McDonald's restaurant into a worldwide fast food empire. For his first eight years, Kroc did not personally draw a paycheck from the company. Everything went back out to helping the initial franchisees be successful. Toward the end of his life, when Kroc was asked which of his many achievements he was most proud of, he didn't speak of his business success but rather of his service success: he helped more people achieve their dreams of financial independence than anyone else who'd ever lived before him. Virtually everyone who started a McDonald's franchise during the Kroc era retired a multimillionaire. Ironically, by not pursuing his own gain, but instead committing himself to helping others succeed, Kroc became one of the world's wealthiest men.

Real leaders are committed to helping

The most effective leaders first and foremost see themselves as servants. In J.R.R. Tolkien's classic trilogy *The Lord of the Rings*, Sam Gamgee wanted nothing more than to serve Frodo. Time and again, he sacrificed his own comfort and security and endangered his very life on behalf of Frodo and their mutual Quest. No leader could ever hope for a more devoted and loving servant. Sam was not motivated by the hope for personal gain or glory, but through a paradox at least as old as the Bible, his selfless devotion to service earned Sam a place of high honor within the Shire. In *The Heart of a Leader* Ken Blanchard wrote that the primary biblical image of a leader was the shepherd. The shepherd follows his flock as they wander, but that does not make him less of a leader, but rather more so.

Servant leaders move stones

In *Up the Organization* (updated as *Further Up the Organization*), Robert Townsend wrote that, *"the best managers think of themselves as playing coaches... A good manager is a blocking back whenever and wherever needed. No job is too menial for him if it helps one of his players advance toward his objective."* A great example of this type of servant leadership is depicted in the historical novel *Gates of Fire* by Steven Pressfield (the story of how 300 Spartans and a handful of allies held off the entire Persian army at the Battle of Thermopylae). In one of my favorite scenes, King Leonidas of Sparta overhears his men arguing about where to build a defensive wall. Leonidas simply sets down his shield, then starts moving rocks. The others take the hint, and the wall is quickly built. In describing the event, Pressfield gives as good a definition of servant leadership as I've ever seen:

> *A king does not abide within his tent while his men bleed and die upon the field. A king does not dine while his men go hungry, nor sleep when they stand at watch upon the wall. A king does not command his men's loyalty through fear nor purchase it with gold; he earns their love by the sweat of his own back and the pains he endures for their sake. That which comprises the harshest burden, a king lifts first and sets down last. A king does not require service of those he leads but provides it to them. He serves them, not they him... A king does not expend his substance to enslave men, but by his conduct and example makes them free.*

See the job description as a floor, not as a ceiling

"It's not my job." "That's not my department." "I don't know." We've all heard, and perhaps have ourselves given, some of the many excuses for not helping out. When service becomes a value rather than an activity, however, we find the motivation and the means to step outside of the box of our job description or departmental boundaries.

When the job description is seen as a ceiling, it places an upper limit on what you are willing to do (and probably also places an upper limit on your potential to grow and advance). But when you see the job description as a floor, it simply outlines the basic set of your responsibilities, to which you add your own special gifts.

Real service might entail sticking your neck out

Sometimes lending a helping hand means taking a step outside of your comfort zone, and perhaps sticking your neck out. Say, for example, an administrative secretary happens to be walking through a patient care unit of a hospital and from inside a patient room hears somebody calling for a nurse. Looking around and seeing that every nurse on the unit is otherwise occupied, that secretary has a choice to make: either take a risk and go talk to that patient, perhaps delaying whatever it was he or she had set out to do, or leave the patient in distress to wait for a "proper authority" to arrive on the scene. This is partly what W. Edwards Deming, the guru of total quality management, had in mind when he made "drive fear out of the workplace" one of his 14 points for TQM: making it safe for people to reach beyond the boundaries of their job descriptions in order to extend a helping hand to others.

Service does not mean doing for others what they should do for themselves

Watch a child who is trying to do something when the parent comes around and starts to do it for them. What will the child say? *"No! Let me do it!"* There is an art to knowing when the greatest help you can give somebody is letting them do something for themselves. If you are a manager, you know that this art lies at the heart of effective delegation.

Don't rescue people from their messes

One of the hardest things in the world is to watch someone get into a big mess and to not bail them out, even if it would be easy for you to do so. Rescuing them might feel like the right thing to do at the time, and certainly makes you feel warm and fuzzy for doing it (especially if you receive the appropriate gratitude for being the savior of the moment), but is quite possibly the worst thing you could do. Rescuing someone from their problem, while making both you and the rescued party feel more comfortable about the situation, could be preventing that person from learning valuable lessons and developing strength of character. Almost any leader can empower someone to succeed (knowing that he or she can step in to prevent an embarrassing failure should the need arise). It is a very special and courageous leader who can empower someone to fail, allow them to fail without being rescued, then transform their failure into a success by sharing the story and its lessons with the rest of the organization. And above all, it takes a special leader to allow people to fail without being branded as failures.

Service recovery

Research has shown that the most loyal customer (or patient or staff member) is often the one who had a serious problem which somebody took the time to resolve. It is when the chips are down, when the customer is furious, that a helpful service attitude, coupled with the corresponding effective action, is most important. It's been well-documented that the most effective advertising medium in the world is a dissatisfied customer, because they will tell everyone they know, and probably quite a few people they don't know. That is not, however, the kind of advertising you want to have! Going above and beyond to resolve the problem and convert the hostile customer into a raving fan is therefore one of the best marketing investments any organization can make

 Rules for the Journey

1) Service begins with a sincere desire to help others, which is then followed up by action. It's an ancient paradox that the person who gives a helping hand often benefits as much or more than the person being helped.

2) *Webster's Dictionary* has two definitions for helpfulness: "1) the property of providing useful assistance; and 2) friendliness evidenced by a kindly and helpful disposition." Service is the combination of what you do and the attitude with which you do it.

3) See your job description as a floor, not a ceiling, as the basic platform upon which you add your own special touches by bringing your particular strengths, talents, and passions to the work.

4) Service does not necessarily mean doing for others what they should do for themselves or rescuing them from the problems they created.

Take-home exercise: Helping one helps two

Think of something that is important to you—something you would really like to have or do. Now, find someone else who wants the same thing, or something similar. Instead of asking them to help you get what you want, go out of your way to help them get what they want. Pay attention: before long, it's quite likely that—from out of the blue—will come the help you need, in ways that never could have been predicted. (Whenever I've helped someone who was searching for a new job, I've advised them to spend four days a week on their own job search and one day a week helping someone else who needs to find a job. Almost without exception, when I hear back from them, they tell me that the one day that they spent helping someone else did more for their own job search than the four days that they spent directly working for themselves.)

> *Q: What do you have to do if you want a hug?*
> *A: Give someone else a hug.*

Extra credit reading

"When you make life easy for others, you become a guardian angel—someone who can be counted on for great work and little hassle. Once you have that reputation, people will give you whatever you want to keep you in their corner."

MARC MYERS: *How to Make Luck*

Something to think about

"Whatever you most need in life, the best way for you to get it is to help someone else get it who needs it even more than you do."

JOE TYE, *Never Fear, Never Quit*

Module #53
The Second Cornerstone of Service
is Charity

"You give but little when you give of your possessions. It is when you give of yourself that you truly give."

KAHLIL GIBRAN

Our goal for this module

To appreciate the paradox of charity—that the one who gives often benefits as much as or more than the one who receives, and to expand the definition of charity to include giving of one's time, giving of one's self.

Remember the story of King Midas? The greedy monarch's lust for wealth was such that one day he made a wish that everything he touched would turn to gold. His wish was granted, and he starved to death, leaving behind a pantry filled with gold. Remember the story of Johnny Appleseed? He crisscrossed the American frontier, creating a legacy that continues to renew itself. Midas learned to his dismay that a treasure hoarded is a treasure diminished, while Johnny Appleseed showed us that a treasure shared is a treasure multiplied.

Charity is a state of mind

The spirit in which something is given away is often more important than the absolute magnitude of what is being given away. The Ben and Jerry's ice cream company is well known for giving corporate funds to worthy causes. What is less well known is that the company got its start by, among other things, giving away ice cream. Many companies give things away, but the special spirit of this company was captured by Fred Lager in his book *Ben & Jerry's: The Inside Scoop*: *"Giving away ice cream came to them [Ben and Jerry] naturally, and they did it without a premeditated calculations to what the payback might be down the road. They truly believe that the joy was in the journey, and were determined to seize upon every opportunity to have fun that came their way."*

Wealth begins with giving

Two of the most successful investors of our age are Warren Buffet and John Marks Templeton. Neither man requires money or recognition for his own sense of authenticity or self-worth, though. Quite the contrary, both have remained modest in their expectations and humble in their outlook. In his book *Riches for the Mind and Spirit,* Templeton wrote: *"Giving, happiness, prayer, and mind power are four building blocks in the foundation of a fulfilled existence on earth."* Notice that money does not make Templeton's list, and the things that do make his list, money cannot buy. Paradoxically, the best way to ultimately grow wealthy is to follow the path of people like Buffet and Templeton—to become authentic and to do your work for the joy of the work, not because you hope it will make you rich and famous.

Don't wait until you strike it rich

"If I won the lottery, I'd give a lot of it to charity." I hear that a lot when I ask people what they would do if they hit the winning number. Of course, American charities are not growing fat from donations being made by lottery winners. Motivational speaker Zig Ziglar gave participants in his programs a little coin-shaped piece of wood that had the letters "tuit" printed on it. Then he would say, *"Now you have a round tuit, so stop saying that someday you'll get around tuit, and do it now."* Don't wait until your money troubles have all been resolved before you decide to support worthwhile charities; that's not likely to ever happen. Many successful people date the beginning of their success to the moment that they made a personal commitment to giving away.

Adopt a lost cause

"Lost causes are the only ones worth fighting for." This was the fatherly advice given to a newly elected U.S. Senator (played by Jimmy Stewart) in the movie *Mr. Smith Goes to Washington.* The poor will always be with us—that's why it's so important to join the fight against world hunger. The killing has been going on for ten thousand years—that's why it's so important to push for world peace. Children will always experiment with cigarette smoking—that's why we must keep fighting tobacco company ad campaigns that make smoking seem cool and glamorous. The cause might be lost, but those who are fighting for the cause sure aren't lost, for in

the fight they find something important about themselves. As Richard Farson put it in his book *Management of the Absurd: Paradoxes in Leadership:*

> ***"Lost causes are the ones most worth fighting for because they tend to be the most important, most humane ones. They require us to live up to the best that is in us, to perfect ourselves and our world. Lost causes cannot be won, but because they are so crucial to us, we nevertheless must try."***

Engage in random acts of generosity

When charity becomes an attitude and not just an action, you will begin to give spontaneously, and you will naturally gravitate toward random acts of generosity. These do not need to be "big deals," they can be simple and anonymous kindnesses. One of my own personal favorites is to drop the coins in my pocket onto the ground; it makes my whole day to see the reaction of a young child picking up a lucky quarter that I've left in front of the grocery store. Another favorite is to stick a dollar bill under the windshield wiper of an old beat-up car.

Be charitable with both money and time

Many successful people attribute the beginning of success to a commitment on their part to give away part of their money, including those who have made a commitment to tithing. But, as Kahlil Gibran wrote in *The Prophet,* you give but little when you give of your time, the greatest gifts are often of yourself. A real spirit of charity will also be reflected in your willingness to give of your time, to put yourself out in the service to others.

Rules for the Journey

1) As you give, so you shall receive. You've heard that, I'm sure, but has it ever occurred to you that many of us have it the other way around? We think that we can't really give until we've first received. But of the ancient wisdom is correct, it's giving that sets the stage for receiving.

2) Charity is the lovely marriage of gratitude, compassion and generosity; it is an attitude more than an act, an opening of the heart more than an opening of the wallet. True charity comes not from a sense of obligation, but rather is given willingly, generously, and in a spirit of spontaneity.

3) Don't wait until your money troubles have all been resolved before you decide to support worthwhile charities. Success will only make you more of who you already are; if you're not generous now, winning the lottery won't make you generous later.

4) Charity begins with an attitude, and a generous attitude begins with a smile. You can give as many of these little gifts away as you want to, and they don't cost you a cent. The more of them you give away, the more of them you seem to have, and the more of them are returned to you.

 Take-home exercise: Be a Johnny Penny Seed

Join the Random Acts of Kindness movement; get into the habit of, every single day, doing some little anonymous kindness for someone who will never be in a position to repay it (at least not directly to you). When you receive change at the store, inconspicuously drop it on the ground. As you do, imagine (with a smile) the reaction of the person who will find it. It might be somebody with serious money troubles who's about to give up on life, and who finds in the "lucky coin" that you've left a sign that a guardian angel is looking over him, and to keep trying for at least one more day. You might get really lucky and see a small child find a quarter that you've left, and be rewarded with a smile the size of Texas. It is ancient wisdom that the pursuit of happiness will leave you empty, while the giving of happiness will fill you up with joy.

Extra credit reading

"A billion dollars in the bank, without the experience of carefreeness and charity, is a state of poverty. Wealth consciousness, by definition, is a state of mind. If you are constantly concerned about how much money you need, then irrespective of the actual dollar amount you have in your account, you are really poor."

DEEPAK CHOPRA: *Creating Affluence*

Something to think about

When it comes to charity, the person doing the giving often benefits more than the person who is receiving.

Module #54
The Third Cornerstone of Service is Compassion

"How far you go in life depends on your being tender with the young, compassionate with the aged, sympathetic with the striving and tolerant of the weak and strong. Because someday in life you will have been all of these."

GEORGE WASHINGTON CARVER

Our goal for this module

To see how compassion really is an element of service, in fact is often the greatest service that one human being can give to another, and to strive in our own lives to replace judgment with compassion.

In his book *Finding Francis, Following Christ*, Michael Crosby recounts the story of how Francis of Assisi's chance encounter with a leper turned out to be a life-transforming experience. For Francis, kissing the hand of the leper sparked a wave of compassion that has influenced generations ever since. This spirit of compassion is captured in the well-known prayer attributed to Saint Francis, the best-loved section of which reads: *"Lord, make me an instrument of your peace; where there is hatred, let me sow love; where there is injury, pardon; where there is doubt, faith; where there is despair, hope; where there is darkness, light; and where there is sadness, joy."*

The paradox of compassion

The paradox of compassion is as old as the world's formative scripture. The real beneficiary of your compassion is not the one to whom you exhibit compassion— were that the case, it would be mere condescension, not genuine compassion. The one who most benefits from the softening of your heart is the one in whose chest that heart is beating. I'm sure there are controlled studies somewhere proving that compassionate people live longer, but all it takes is a bit of observation to prove the point that their years are fuller. Especially since 9/11, our world has become more polarized along political, racial, and religious lines. It behooves us to remember, as Mother Teresa put it, that we are all children of the same god. Sibling rivalry might be natural, but it should be tempered with family compassion and love.

Genuine compassion entails mutuality

One of the first lessons Bill W learned in founding Alcoholics Anonymous was that trying to help another alcoholic stay sober never worked, because the supposed recipient of that help was usually too proud or defensive to accept it. What did work, however, was when the would-be sponsor explained that he needed to help the drunk as much as the drunk needed to be helped, because the best way for a recovering alcoholic to remain sober is by helping others achieve sobriety. The offering of help isn't really compassionate if it's given with condescension rather than a spirit of mutuality.

The tough guy paradox

Make my day. We love our Hollywood tough guys. Unfortunately, too many managers assume that because it works on the silver screen, it will also work in the workplace. Real leaders (as opposed to the Hollywood kind) are much more interested in building people up than they are in tearing them down. Tough guys like Donald Trump and Chainsaw Al Dunlap are more likely to end up bankrupt and/or in disgrace than they are to sustain success over a long period of time. And here's the ultimate irony—managers who act as though "intimidation" and "humiliation" are synonyms for "motivation" are not merely despised—they are laughed at behind their backs. Especially after they fail, which they eventually will do.

Join the Dignitarian movement

Robert Fuller is on a mission to end what he calls "rankism" in the world. He is the author of the book entitled *Somebodies and Nobodies*. Fuller says that while rank is both and necessary and inevitable, the abuse of rank is not acceptable. A boss who intimidates and humiliates employees is engaged in rankism, as is a nurse who gossips about patients in the break room. Of course, at one time or another, we are all a somebody and we are all a nobody. The abusive boss of today can end up the ignored nursing home patient of tomorrow. The solution to the problem of rankism is compassion. And the higher you are on the pyramid, the more you owe it to the people below you to treat them with compassion, respect, and dignity.

Stop the gossip

Making conversation by putting others down (which is always what gossip is about) is an insidious habit that is easy to fall into and very hard to break out of. When I read the book *Gossip: Ten Pathways to Eliminate It from Your Life and Transform Your Soul* by Lori Palatnik and Bob Burg, it was a real wake-up call. I have never considered myself a gossip, and for over ten years have tried assiduously to keep a rein on habitual judgmentalism. I did not realize the extent to which what I thought were innocent comments—or just sitting quietly as other people made such comments—could be so harmful. And not only harmful to person who is the object of the comments—harmful to those making them. So for your own sake, if not others, stop the gossip.

Leaders must promote positive compassion

In my seminars, the question I am most frequently asked goes something like this: *"I am trying to be positive myself, but the negativity of people around me always drags me down. What can I do to keep a positive attitude in a negative environment?"* I believe this question reflects a failure of leadership in that individual's organization. It is a leader's *responsibility* to create the conditions for a positive workplace environment, and then to expect and demand that people act in a way that honors compassion, respect, and dignity. This is, of course, important for excellence customer service (and quality patient care in healthcare organizations). It's also good for the bottom line. But most important, it's imperative for the quality of life for people who work there. Toxic emotional negativity is malignant, and it is contagious. It drags people down, and cannot help but be a negative influence on their families.

Rules for the Journey

1) Compassion, according to *Webster's Dictionary*, means "a feeling of deep sympathy and sorrow for another who is stricken by misfortune, accompanied by a strong desire to alleviate the suffering." Consider the fact that at some point or another, all of us are so stricken. Anyone you meet might need compassion. Indeed, on many an occasion the greatest service that you can render to another human being is the simple gift of compassion.

2) Catch yourself before you judge others on the basis of such superficial factors as physical appearance or what they happen to do for a living. To be compassionate is to honor the soul that lives underneath appearances.

3) My favorite definition of charisma is this—it's the ability to make someone else feel special. And one of the best ways to make someone feel special is to slow down and listen, really listen, when they're talking.

4) Genuine compassion entails mutuality, an understanding that service is a bilateral relationship; the hospital is a great metaphor, because caregivers need patients as much as patients need caregivers.

Take-home exercise: Make people feel important

Mary Kay Ash (founder of the cosmetics company that bears her name) used to tell her beauty consultants that they should visualize the letters MMFI stenciled across the foreheads of people they were speaking with—*Make Me Feel Important*. That is the best formula I know for compassion: making other people feel important, making them feel special. It is also the best formula I know for leadership charisma; it has nothing whatsoever to do with the leader and everything to do with how that leader makes other people feel. Charismatic leaders are those who have the ability to make other people feel important, to make them feel special. And bringing the paradox of compassion full circle, the more you go out of your way to make other people feel important and special, the more important and special you will feel yourself.

Extra credit reading

"The joy that compassion brings is one of the best-kept secrets of humanity. It is a secret known to only a very few people, a secret that has to be rediscovered over and over again."

HENRI J.M. NOUWEN: *Here and Now*

Something to think about

Action puts the Passion into Compassion; without action, compassion is no more than good intentions.

Module #55
The Fourth Cornerstone of Service is Renewal

"So as long as a person is capable of self-renewal, they are a living being."

HENRI FREDERIC AMIEL

Our goal for this module

To see that not only is making the time for personal renewal not a waste of time, but that it is absolutely necessary for us to continue in our ability to be of service to others—and then to make the commitment to make the time.

It's one of the enduring myths of the ages: the hero retreats into the desert, or falls into the abyss, and returns stronger and wiser. Like the hero of myth, we all must make the time for renewal. Whether it is making a journey into the desert of metaphor, or dealing with the abyss of our own adversity, a commitment to periodic reflection and renewal can help us become stronger and wiser (and perhaps even more heroic).

The voyage of renewal

One of the beautiful things about setting out on a personal voyage of renewal is that you can never be quite sure of what you'll find, but you can usually bet it will be more than you bargained for—in the very best sense of that notion. Periodic self-renewal is essential to your continued growth as a person. As the *I Ching* noted more than two thousand years ago, just as a well needs to periodically be taken out of service to be relined, so too a person must periodically retreat from the daily buzz for reflection and renewal. You can't pour out of an empty pitcher. If you wish to make a lifetime devotion to serving others, you must also make a commitment to renewing yourself, to refilling your pitcher. In the healthcare professions, the question is often asked, *"Who cares for the caregiver?"* It's a question we all should ask of ourselves. The ultimate answer is that the caregiver must take personal responsibility for not allowing his or her own pitcher to become so depleted that it can no longer pour forth.

Ask for help, then be willing to receive it

Have you ever met anyone who combined a real commitment to serving others with a martyr complex for the sacrifices that this service required? Or perhaps been that person yourself? That is someone who is headed for inevitable burnout. Here is a great suggestion for avoiding it: practice The Golden Rule in Reverse—be willing to do for yourself at least as much as you are willing to do for others. Ask for help when you find yourself overloaded, and make the time (*make it* because you're unlikely to find it) to enjoy the beauty of nature and the abundance of your community. In our Lone Ranger culture, it's difficult for many of us to ask for the help we need, especially if it implies some sort of weakness on our part. Nevertheless, renewal—the refilling of the pitcher—often requires that we do just that. It also requires that when others offer to help (including perhaps unwelcome suggestions) we accept their help, making the assumption that they are offering it in good faith and with our best interest at heart.

Renewal and your mental models

The single-most important determinant of your "reality" is not in fact the factual reality of the outside world, but rather the internalized mental module with which you interpret that reality. In their book *The Power of Impossible Thinking*, Yoram Wind and Colin Crook share many examples of how changing mental models resulted in changing reality. It's not easy to change your mental models. But when you *do* change them, perhaps through a period of introspection and renewal, amazing insights can occur and wonderful things can happen. What mental models might be holding you back preventing you from exploring the boundaries of your own potential. Why don't you get out of the box and try on a new model?

Renewal and redirection

You might have heard or read a motivational type saying that you can be anything you want to be (if you are willing to pay the price). Well, both common sense and personal experience tell you that's simply not the case. It's motivational hyperbole.

In fact, one of the worst things for you to do is try to become someone you're not in hopes of striking it rich or making it big. At some time or another, the greatest service you will ever perform for yourself is to discover the Authentic You, and then to commit yourself to being great at being the person you are meant to be, and not what you think the rest of the world expects you to be. A period of time devoted to reflection and renewal can pay enormous dividends to your career and to your personal life.

Seek sources of renewal outside your territory

I am not in the real estate business, but one of the most helpful books I've read for building my own business is *The Millionaire Real Estate Agent* by Gary Keller. One of the most insightful books I've read on the subject of leadership is *The Lord of the Rings* by J.R.R. Tolkien. The greatest creative breakthroughs often occur when you get outside of your usual box. Go to a different church (or if you're not a church-goer, go to any church) with an open mind and see what you bring home with you. Go with a friend to a meeting of AA or other support group—you might find yourself every bit as inspired as the support group members themselves. Listen to Bach instead of Bono (or vice versa) and see if it doesn't spark something new in your soul.

Renewal does not necessarily mean change

When a couple renews their wedding vows, the renewal is not a change—it's a re-commitment to something tried and true. Renewal often implies refocusing and recommitting more than it does making a change. It means thinking about what really matters, and then making the commitment to devote more time and energy to those things, and less time and energy on things that really don't matter. And just as a pitcher is strongest at the place where it was once broken and has been glued back together, quite often people are strongest at those points where they had once seemed broken and, through a process of renewal, turned weakness to strength.

Rules for the Journey

1) You cannot pour from an empty pitcher. People who do not take time for renewal, who do not take care of themselves, often end up cynical, burned out, and frankly not very caring.

2) A voyage of renewal is an adventure; you can never be sure of what you'll find or where you'll end up, but you can be sure that you will grow stronger and wiser through the journey.

3) Practice the golden rule in reverse—do for yourself at least as much as you're willing to do for others. Ask for help when you're overloaded, and make the time for reflection and rejuvenation.

4) If we're paying attention, times of difficulty or adversity are (often well-disguised) opportunities for renewal. One reason that most people who have ever lost a job will look back and say it was the best thing that could have happened is that it can force the introspection and redirection that is central to the renewal process.

Take-home exercise: Renew with rituals

Incorporate little renewal rituals into your daily routine; two of my favorites are a quick exercise routine and fast walk after lunch, and listening to classical music while I read in the evenings. When I can get away with it, I include a nap in my daily rituals. We once had rituals for everything, but today we're too busy. Restoring the simple practice of rituals—like lighting candles before dinner or saying a prayer before bed—can be enormously renewing.

Extra credit reading

"It is my belief that each personality does already have a quiet center within, which is never disturbed, and is unmoved, like the mathematical point in the very center of a wheel or axle which remains stationary. What we need to do is to find this quiet center within us and retreat into it periodically for rest, recuperation, and renewed vigor."

MAXWELL MALTZ: *Psycho-Cybernetics*

Something to think about

If you're not enjoying the journey, the destination will be a disappointment.

MCZEN

At one time the words "servant leadership" would have been considered an oxymoron (in fact, some leaders still act as if that were the case). But in one organization after another, it's been proven that the most successful leaders are those who first and foremost see themselves as servants, not as served.

Core Action Value #12 is Leadership

Management is a job description; leadership is a life decision. And in today's complex world, organizations need leadership in every corner, not just in the corner office. When leadership is an attitude and a way of life, not just something that's a part of your job description, it becomes a value in its own right. In many respects, leadership closes the circle of The Twelve Core Action Values by bringing us back to Authenticity. The most effective leaders become leaders not because of a need to have followers, or for money and power—these are byproducts. They become leaders because of a need to pursue authentic goals that inspire others as well as themselves.

Cornerstone #1: Expectations

Values-based leaders are committed to creating better organizations and contributing to a better world, and thus they have high expectations for themselves and for the people they lead.

Cornerstone #2: Example

Leaders are judicious in their words, enthusiastic in their actions, and committed to their missions because they know that they speak more forcefully by who they are than by what they say.

Cornerstone #3: Encouragement

Leaders encourage us to do our best and to be our best, to persevere through the inevitable obstacles and setbacks, and to work together in a spirit of fellowship toward the realization of a shared vision.

Cornerstone #4: Celebration

Leaders help us celebrate our victories, and our defeats; they celebrate with us the important passages of work and life; and they use celebrations as the platform from which to launch renewed efforts toward ever-larger goals.

"Trust and protect your people, nurture their growth and development, and lay the foundation upon which they can achieve greatness after you pass the torch of leadership on to them."

JOE TYE: *Leadership Lessons: What You Can Learn from J.R.R. Tolkien's Classic Works*

Module #56
Core Action Value #12 is Leadership

"Leaders are not born; they are made. And they are made just like anything else—through hard work."

VINCE LOMBARDI

Our goal for this module

To understand the distinction between management and leadership, and to appreciate that at one time or another, we all have the opportunity, and the obligation, to serve in a leadership role.

Because of the nature of my work, I am occasionally referred to as a "Pollyanna." I take this as the highest compliment, because Pollyanna was a true leader. At the beginning of the story, she came into a community that was fractured, polarized and riven with hatred. But Pollyanna expected the best from people, no matter how they had behaved in the past; she set an example of positive caring; she encouraged people to reconnect with each other; and she celebrated all that is right with life. By story's end, broken relationships had been healed, hatred had transformed into fellowship, and people began looking toward a positive future rather than wallowing around in memories of the dead past. That is leadership at its very best.

Leadership is the culmination of the first Eleven Core Action Values

Anyone who really takes to heart and acts upon Core Action Values 1-11 will, almost inevitably, be looked up to, and act as a leader. That's why *The Twelve Core Action Values* is the ultimate course in values-based leadership.

CAV 1 ➜ CAV 11 = CAV 12

Management is a job description, leadership is a life decision

There are various distinctions between management and leadership, such as this one: management is doing things right, leadership is doing the right thing. There is also obvious overlap between the two. Here's my take on it: I think of management as a job description; your organization can make you a manager by giving you a title, a new set of responsibilities (and hopefully a pay raise). Leadership, by contrast, is a life decision; it is the ongoing commitment to seek opportunities to improve upon the status quo, and then to take the initiative to make those improvements. Throughout history, some of the most effective leaders did not have formal titles, they simply saw what needed to be done and took it upon themselves to do it.

Learn to follow, then to lead

One who presumes to lead must first learn to follow. Especially on a high-performance work team, the role of "leader" will often change from one person to another, depending upon the particular challenge. Unfortunately, while there are many courses and books on leadership, followership gets short shrift; a Google search yields more than 1,500 items on leadership for every one item on followership. That's too bad, because being a great follower is the best possible training for being a great leader. As Ira Chaleff says in the book *Courageous Followership*, the best followers both challenge and support their leaders. For the leader, this means being aware of how your leadership style can either encourage or intimidate people, and creating mechanisms that allow people to challenge inappropriate policies, stupid decisions, and unacceptable behavior in a way that is both safe and constructive. For the follower, it means taking ownership for the role and responsibilities. Chaleff says: *"Successful followers care passionately about their work and the people it serves. They have a sense of ownership, of stewardship... Armchair critics have little influence with the leader and group whereas team members passionately fulfilling a role can weigh in heavily."*

Transforming leadership is a bilateral relationship

In his Pulitzer Prize-winning book *Leadership*, James MacGregor Burns distinguished between *transactional leadership*, which he defined as the management necessary to run an organization, and *transforming leadership*, which he defined as leadership that transforms people by raising them to a higher level of values and expectations. He also wrote that transforming leadership is a bilateral relationship in which *both* followers and leader are transformed. To be a transforming leader, therefore, one must be an active listener and willing follower, and be willing to change and to grow.

You build a winning team with winning players

Values-based leaders know that the non-negotiable first step to building a winning team is helping individual team members develop the attitudes and the skills required to think and act like a winning player. One of the best ways of investing in your people is sharing what you have learned yourself through this course on *The Twelve Core Action Values*.

A leadership paradigm for the 21st century

During the second half of the 20th century, the predominant management paradigm followed what I call the 2P+2C formula: Predict and Plan, then Command and Control. This tended toward centralized, top-down, disempowering organizational structures. Today, the world is far too complex and turbulent to specifically predict and plan for the future, and the best people do not want to work in a place where they are commanded and controlled. I believe the most effective leadership paradigm for the 21st century will follow the 2V+OE formula. Leaders will inculcate a commitment to core Values and a shared Vision, then encourage people to take Ownership for their role in living those values and achieving that vision, and to Empower themselves to take the initiative to be full partners in the process.

$$2P+2C \rightarrow 2V+OE$$

 ## Rules for the Journey

1) Leadership becomes a value in and of itself when it is not just an activity in a job description, but rather a philosophy and a way of life; the essential skills of leadership are first learned by practicing the skills of great followership.

2) A leader takes you to a place you didn't know you wanted to go; that implies both the vision itself and the ability to inspire others to work toward the fulfillment of that vision.

3) Build a winning team by teaching individual team members the skills and attitudes needed to think and act like winning players.

4) Real leaders are committed for the long-haul; they don't quit when faced with the obstacles and setbacks that are inevitable in any endeavor that is worth achieving.

5) As James A. Autry says in his book *Love and Profit*, leadership is largely a matter of love and caring—a commitment to creating a community of people committed to each other and to the achievement of common goals.

 ## Take-home exercise: See yourself as the CEO of Me, Inc.

Here's a great way to cultivate leadership as a value: think of yourself as the chief executive officer of an organization consisting of just one person—you. As CEO of Me, Inc., you are responsible for creating and marketing the best possible product (e.g. your education, your resume, your personal website); you are responsible for building your team (e.g. financial planner, personal coach, spiritual guide); you are responsible for perceiving and pursuing opportunities (e.g. helping your organization be more positive and productive, taking a leadership role in service and community organizations, encouraging your children to reach higher in their goals and aspirations). Thinking of yourself as CEO of You, Inc. will help you think more like a leader in every other dimension of your life as well.

 ## Extra credit reading

"Whatever your role in life may be, you make a difference. There is a 100 percent chance that you can be a role model for leadership. There is a 100 percent chance that you can influence someone else's performance. There is a 100 percent chance that you can affect what someone else thinks, says, and does. There is a 100 percent chance that you will make a difference in other people's lives."

JAMES KOUZES AND BARRY POSNER: *A Leader's Legacy*

Something to think about

Confucius on leadership character

The superior person works to develop the superior aspects of his character. The small person allows the inferior aspects his of character to flourish.

The superior person is easy to serve but difficult to please. The small person is difficult to serve but easy to please.

The superior person can see a question from all sides. The small person can see it only from a biased perspective.

The superior person calls attention to the good points in others. The small person calls attention to their defects.

The superior person can influence those who are above her. The small person can influence only those below her.

The demands that the superior person makes are on himself. The demands of the small person are placed upon others.

The superior person is slow in word but prompt in deed. The small person is quick to make promises but slow to keep them.

The superior person is diligent in ascertaining what is right. The small person is diligent in ascertaining what will pay.

The superior person is calm and at ease. The small person is fretful and ill at ease.

When things go wrong, the superior person seeks blame in herself. When things go wrong, the small person seeks blame in others.

The small person thinks he is a superior person. The superior person knows he is a small person.

In the presence of a superior person, think all the time how you might equal him. In the presence of a small person, evaluate your own character to be sure you are not like him.

The superior person has the quality of wind. The small person has the quality of grass. When the wind blows, the grass cannot help but to bend.

CONFUCIUS: *The Analects*

Module #57
The First Cornerstone of Leadership is Expectations

"If you treat people the way they are, you make them worse. If you treat them the way they ought to be, you make them capable of becoming what they ought to be."

JOHAN WOLFGANG VON GOETHE

Our goal for this module

To appreciate the power of positive expectations for fostering self-fulfilling prophecies, to understand that we should expect values-based behaviors from ourselves and others, and to raise our own sites and standards with more meaningful goals.

There is a scene early in J.R.R. Tolkien's book *The Hobbit* that sets the stage for the entire story. Gandalf the wizard has agreed to help Thorin and his band of dwarves recover the treasure that was stolen from them by a fire-breathing dragon. The dragon has hoarded the treasure deep in a cavern at the bottom of a mountain, and the dwarves need a burglar to sneak in to tell them where the dragon is so they can recover the treasure without being caught. Gandalf introduces them to Bilbo Baggins, the hobbit. Now, hobbits are short and fat and they love nothing more than eating, drinking and sleeping. Thorin, the mighty king of the dwarves, looks down at the little hobbit and sniffs, *"Why, he looks more like a grocer than a burglar."* Gandalf replies that there's more to Bilbo than meets the eye, that in fact there's more to him than even he sees in himself. The rest of the story *is* the story of little Bilbo Baggins striving to live up to the expectation created for him by Gandalf the wizard at the very start. By story's end, it is Bilbo who has become the real leader of the group.

You tend to get what you expect, so expect the best

In a recent research project, subjects were asked to rate the flavor of two glasses of wine. They were told that one was from a very expensive bottle and the other from an inexpensive bottle. In every instance, they rated the expensive wine as having superior flavor. In fact, both glasses had been poured from the same bottle—people thought one tasted better because they *expected* it to taste better. This is a principle that is almost as ironclad as the law of gravity: you tend to get what you expect to get out of life. Over time, optimists achieve great results while pessimists do not. In medicine it's called the Placebo Effect, in management it's called the Pygmalion Effect, but the principles are the same: your outcomes are substantially influenced by your expectations. That's why values-based leaders have high expectations for themselves and for the people they work with, and have little tolerance for the pessimists who seem to relish the prospect of failure so they can say, *"see, I told you it would never work."*

Values-based leaders expect people to know and to live the organization's values

Most organizations have (or should have) a written statement of values. Far fewer, however, really expect people to know by heart what those values are, much less what is expected of each individual when it comes to actually living them. That reflects a failure on the part of the organization's leaders to demonstrate a commitment to values-based leadership. People *should* know, believe in, and act upon the values of the organization they are a part of. Auto-Owners Insurance is a Fortune 500 company and longstanding Values Coach client. The company has ten core values (honesty, hard work, prudence, loyalty, the team, relationships, opportunities for associates, the customer, stability and consistency, and profit), and it expects *every* associate to know and to live those values—no exceptions. In my travels with the company, I've randomly asked hundreds of associates to recite these ten values for me, from memory. They have different ways of remembering them, but almost everyone is able to tell me all ten. Not only that, they do so with obvious pride. If I ask for specifics—for example, by asking what the tolerance level is for bending the honesty value (answer: zero)—they respond in a way that tells me they've obviously thought about it. In this regard, Auto-Owners stands as a model for every organization that has not put this sort of effort into defining and enforcing its values.

Be a Dionarap

The paranoid believes that nobody likes him and that everyone is out to get him. The Dionarap (the word paranoid spelled backwards) assumes that everyone likes her and wants to help her succeed. According to what psychologists call the law of reciprocity, people respond in kind to the emotions you project to them (in other words, if you don't like someone, they probably won't like you). Being a Dionarap is far more likely to contribute to your effectiveness as a leader than would being a paranoid. Not only that, it's far more likely to help you make friends, help you promote your ideas and your services, and cultivate a more positive and productive organization. Of course, there might well be someone who really is out to get you. To be a Dionarap does not mean to be naïve or stupid—it means to give people the benefit of the doubt before you judge their actions or make assumptions about their motives.

Be realistic—expect miracles

In his book *Weird Ideas that Work: 11 ½ Practices for Promoting, Managing, and Sustaining Innovation*, Stanford engineering professor Robert Sutton says that more than 500 studies have been conducted on the power of self-fulfilling prophecy. He says this research shows that positive expectations can create confidence, and that confident people perform better. *"These studies,"* he says, *"find that, independent of other factors, when leaders believe their subordinates will perform well, positive expectations lead to better performance. And the converse holds for [low expectations and] poor performance."* Sutton cites several examples of "impossible" projects that have succeeded, while acknowledging that expectation alone does not necessarily transform itself into reality. Quoting John Gardner, Sutton says that *"the prime function of a leader is to keep hope alive."* For the values-based leader, there is no such thing as false hope!

> ***Decide to do something that will probably fail, then convince yourself and everyone else that success is certain.***
>
> ROBERT I. SUTTON: *Weird Ideas that Work*

Expectations are created through dialog

In the book *Hope Is Not a Method*, two former army commanders describe lessons they say American business leaders can learn from the experience of the U.S. military in its rebuilding during the years after the Vietnam War. One of those lessons is that commanders do not simply tell people what to do and expect them to do it. Rather, goals evolve through dialogue. As Kevin Eikenberry writes in his book *Remarkable Leadership: Unleashing Your Leadership Potential One Skill at a Time*:

> *Teams can't gain the clear direction they need without conversation. A PowerPoint presentation may start the conversation, but it shouldn't be all there is. It is the responsibility of leadership to provide that opportunity for conversation. This conversation creates the understanding that teams need to clarify their goals and make the decisions about how they will deal with the opportunities and challenges that they inevitably will encounter as they do their work.*

Simplify the vision

Whether the leadership task is running a scout troop, a company, or a nation, the most effective leaders have the ability to communicate a powerful and complex vision in terms that anyone can understand. Martin Luther King made the case against segregation in his lengthy, complex, and thoroughly-documented *"Letter from the Birmingham Jail;"* he also made the vision powerfully accessible to the general public in his *I Have a Dream* speech, which lasted under five minutes. In *Good to Great*, Collins compared the companies which made the leap to corporate stardom with similar companies that did not. One of the most important differences was that organizations in the former group were able to organize around a simple guiding concept, whereas those in the latter group tended to make things much too complicated.

Prepare people for change

Leadership expert James O'Toole likens management in today's organizations to running a fire department. In today's fast-changing world, there is no way you can anticipate every potential scenario, and to expect that every decision will be made by "the boss," would lead to disaster. Instead, people must be given the skills and the confidence to empower themselves to make the appropriate decisions in each situation, just as firefighters can never rehearse a specific fire, but only prepare themselves for whatever fire might come along. One of the surest ways to prepare people for the challenges of leadership is to teach them—both through your personal example and your communication efforts—how to live *The Twelve Core Action Values.*

> **People are *not* afraid of change—people *love* change, so long as it comes with a guaranty of being a change for the better. What they *are* afraid of is the uncertainty that goes with change. Creating the expectation of positive outcomes is one of the best ways of helping people deal with change.**

Believe in your destiny

One of the things great leaders do is create a sense of destiny. When Roosevelt called for the unconditional surrender of Germany and Japan in World War II, he fostered the perception that total victory was not only possible, it was inevitable. When Kennedy called for putting a man on the moon, we all just knew it was going to happen, even after Kennedy himself was no longer there to provide leadership. At the start, the leader must absolutely believe that the goal is honorable and attainable, if not inevitable, and be personally committed to doing everything possible in its pursuit. After that, the sense of destiny is intensified through a complex interaction between leader and followers.

Expect the best but prepare for the worst

It is easier to expect the best if you are prepared for the worst. As many a banker has told many an entrepreneur, if you take care of the downside the upside will take care of itself.

Rules for the Journey

1) Effective leaders expect a lot from themselves and from others. They create optimism that those expectations can be achieved, and give people the training, the tools, and the support they need to achieve them.

2) The acid test of leadership is imbuing people with a transcendent sense a purpose and meaning in the work itself. People didn't march with Martin Luther King because they wanted to take a walk.

3) Leaders are clear in communicating their performance expectations, and quick to let people know when those expectations are not being met, but they also appreciate that the most important expectations are not dictated, but rather created through dialog.

4) Deal with the uncertainty that creates resistance to change by equipping people with the skills they need to cope with anxiety, and by creating the expectation of a successful outcome for every change initiative.

5) Expect the best, prepare for the worst. The more prepared you are for the worst to happen, the more likely it is that the best will happen instead.

Take-home exercise: Replace the tyranny of OR with the genius of AND

One of the characteristics of the "visionary companies" described by Collins and Porras in *Built to Last* was that they replaced the tyranny of OR with the genius of AND. They were not, for example, willing to accept a tradeoff between cost and quality; to allow customer service to suffer in the pursuit of productivity; or to reduce investments in research and marketing to accommodate a recessionary economy. By holding themselves to high expectations at all times, these companies create the sort of "can do" environment in which the impossible only takes a little longer.

Most of us settle for the tyranny of OR in our work and personal lives, often without even being aware of it. We assume there must be a tradeoff between a successful career and time with family; that there must be a tradeoff between responsibly planning for retirement and enjoying life in the present; that there must be a tradeoff between doing the things we want to do and doing the things we must do.

For this exercise, make a list of all the possible areas in which you are making such tradeoffs. For each one, imagine a way that you might substitute the genius of AND. So, for example, you could decide that instead of taking an expensive vacation to Las Vegas, you can take that vacation hiking one of our glorious national parks, and put the thousands of dollars you'd save into your retirement fund. And here's the best part: chances are that you'd enjoy hiking a lot more than sitting in front of a slot machine (not to mention that it would be a lot better for your health, both physical and mental).

 ## Extra credit reading

"In my years of research on human achievement and accomplishment, one of the most striking things I've learned is that a high expectation of success is the single most valuable quality you can bring into any challenging situation. A high expectation of success is more important than natural ability or the lack thereof. It's more important than practice or preparation. This has been proven in any number of controlled experiments."

DENIS WAITLEY: *The New Dynamics of Winning*

Something to think about

If you want to achieve success beyond your wildest expectations, you have to begin with wild expectations.

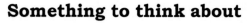

Module #58
The Second Cornerstone of Leadership is Example

"The skilled commander seeks victory from the situation and does not demand it of his subordinates."

SUN TZU

Our goal for this module

To think about what it means for the values-based leader to lead by example, and to make the personal commitment to be such a leader, using *The Twelve Core Action Values* as a foundation.

As Alexander the Great was leading his army through the blistering Parthian desert, men were literally dying of thirst. When one of his lieutenants brought him a helmet half-filled with water, Alexander asked if the other men had all drunk yet. On being told that they hadn't, and that this was the only water anywhere, he ostentatiously turned the helmet upside down and poured the water into the sand. During the U.S. Civil War, General Ulysses S. Grant wore the uniform of an ordinary foot soldier; he once evacuated his own headquarters so the building could be used to house wounded soldiers. Mahatma Gandhi liberated India from British rule by setting an example of nonviolent resistance, an example that was later emulated by Martin Luther King in the fight against segregation and by Nelson Mandela in the fight against apartheid. It's been said that there are only three types of leadership—example, example, and example. Values-based leaders lead by example.

Values-based leadership begins with character

"Character is destiny," said the ancient Greek philosopher Heraclitus. You might have heard that one definition of character is what you do when no one else can see you. For the values-based leader, a variation on that theme is assuming that everyone can always see you. Sometimes it won't be easy, and sometimes it won't feel natural; you will find yourself having to do things that you really don't want to do (and that no one else is making you do), and at other times you will find yourself not doing things that you really want to do (and that no one else would know about were you to do them). Remember, there is no character gene. Character is built stone-by-stone, with each action you take or don't take; by the way you treat other people; and by the thoughts you allow into your head. The best course on character you could possibly take, and the most effective formula for building character you could possibly follow, is to internalize, operationalize, and incorporate into your life the principles of *The Twelve Core Action Values*.

Practice FILO leadership

First in, last out (FILO) is one method of inventory control management. It is also a great philosophy for values-based leadership. Let's look at an example. The Israeli army practices what is called the Palmach Doctrine, which means that officers are always in front during an attack, and that officers make up the rearguard in the event of a retreat. This has two important benefits. First, when leaders lead from the front, they earn more intense loyalty than if they command from the rear. Second, officers are much less likely to order suicide charges if they know that they will be leading the attack, and are much less inclined to order a withdrawal if they know they'll be the last one out. That is a pretty good metaphor for leadership by example. In his novel *Gates of Fire*, about the epic battle of Thermopylae (quoted above), Steven Pressfield says that leaders are first to pick up the heaviest burden and last to lay them down. That is as good a description as I've read for servant leadership, for leadership by example.

Share your courage with others, keep your fears to yourself

Jonathan Swift said "share your courage with others, keep your fears to yourself" because he understood that both fear and courage are contagious. The emotional state displayed by the leader (fear or courage) can ripple throughout a team or an organization, and influence the outcome for better or worse. Dennis N. T. Perkins, in his book *Leading at the Edge: Leadership Lessons from the Extraordinary Saga of Shackleton's Antarctic Expedition* expressed it this way:

> *There are times in which leaders need to maintain their composure, despite the natural inclination to express feelings of discouragement, fear, or even despair. This is not to say that they should shield others from reality or withhold basic information about the situation. Rather, it is to say that there are times... in which the perceived attitude of the leader is a powerful force that can create energy and optimism or fear and pessimism: It becomes a self-fulfilling prophecy.*

Leadership entails voluntary loss of freedom

When you are a leader (this includes being in any management position) you must give up certain freedoms: the freedom to be negative; the freedom to second guess administrative decisions after they've been made (hopefully with your input if your areas of responsibility are involved); the freedom to be a naysayer, since your pessimism can contribute to a self-fulfilling prophecy of failure; and the freedom to slack off when it comes to making a sincere effort to live *The Twelve Core Action Values*, since your example has a profound influence on those who look up to you. It is a paradox that in these respects, leaders have *less* freedom than followers do.

 ## Rules for the Journey

1) More than anything, real leadership is about living your values; in this regard, *The Twelve Core Action Values* provide an trustworthy roadmap for becoming the best type of leader—one who leads by example.

2) Leadership begins with a state of mind. Anyone can be a leader if they pay attention to opportunities to make a contribution and to make a difference—and then take the initiative to do something about it. Do that and people will follow your lead.

3) To assume a position of leadership means giving up many freedoms: the freedom to criticize, complain, and gossip; the freedom to point fingers; the freedom to be a pessimist; the freedom to say "it's not my job."

4) One of the most important, and difficult, duties of leadership is to invite critical feedback and then to listen openly; the leader's willingness to do this sets the tone for everyone else in the organization.

5) Through his or her own example, the values-based leader establishes an ironclad expectation that everyone in your organization will treat others with respect, humility and dignity.

 ## Take-home exercise: Set a great example by following one

Think of the people you most admire as leaders. They could be historical or contemporary, world leaders or leaders in your community. Make a list of five key characteristics about these men and women for which you have included them in your pantheon of great leaders. Now write down five phrases that best describe your leadership style. Compare the two lists. What can you learn from the example of the leaders you admire that can help you make modifications to your own approach to leadership. In other words, how can these exemplary leaders help you set a better example yourself?

 ## Extra credit reading

"Investing in people and building their skills and abilities raises their sense of their own competency and capability. To the extent people believe they are better prepared and more skilled, they will perform at a higher level simply because they have more confidence in themselves, including a belief in their ability to learn and develop that encourages further learning and growth."

JEFFREY PFEFFER: *What Were They Thinking? Unconventional Wisdom About Management*

In J.R.R. Tolkien's classic *The Lord of the Rings*, when Aragorn offered to be the hobbits' guide on their dangerous quest, he promised that he would put his life on the line to protect their lives. He never stepped back from that promise—not once. In return, he earned their undying loyalty, and his example reinforced the hobbits' own "life or death" commitment to one another. How many employees of American corporations really feel that their bosses would go to the mat for them? Do the people who look up to you as a leader feel like you would go to the mat for them?

Module #59
The Third Cornerstone of Leadership is Encouragement

"The greatest asset of any society is the talent and energy of its people. Yet no society has ever fully recognized or honored that asset; indeed, most societies have effectively stifled both talent and energy. The release of human possibilities is one of the most basic of social objectives and leadership goals."

JOHN W. GARDNER

Our goal for this module

To appreciate the often underappreciated importance of encouragement as both an element of effective leadership, and of cultivating optimal personal and organizational achievement.

"We have nothing to fear but fear itself." "We shall never surrender." **Franklin D. Roosevelt and Winston Churchill were masters at encouraging their people to persevere during the darkest days of the Great Depression and World War II. When John F. Kennedy challenged us to put a man on the moon by the end of the sixties, he galvanized a nation and launched a technological revolution. With his famous (or infamous) "reality distortion field," Steve Jobs has encouraged one small band after another of Silicon Valley rebels to revolutionize the computer, music, motion picture, and telecommunications industries. That's what leaders do: they encourage us in the traditional sense of the word meaning to instill courage in our hearts, and they encourage us in the more contemporary sense of the word to urge us forward to tackle those challenges that once might have seemed to be impossible.**

Leaders encourage us to be our best selves

The best leaders start with holding us to high expectations, and then encourage us to live up to those expectations. They encourage us to take the basket off of our inner candles and to share our gifts with the world, to stop settling for anemic dreams and goals, and to become our meant-to-be best selves. One of the best descriptions of the encouraging leader is that given by Les Brown in his book *Live Your Dreams*:

> ***I believe the most important thing you can sell people is a belief in themselves. The most significant investment you can make is one in your own potential for greatness, and your own capacity to make a difference in the lives of those around you.***

Learn to tell stories

From the dawn of human civilization, humans have told stories to teach, to encourage and inspire, to sell, and to transmit values from one generation to the next. More than anything, we resonate with our leaders because of the stories they tell. As Howard Gardner says in *Leading Minds: An Anatomy of Leadership*, *"Leaders achieve their effectiveness chiefly through the stories they relate."* It's astonishing, really, that we don't teach the art of story-telling in the college core curriculum. But that being the case, you need to cultivate the skill on your own. And to be sure, it is a skill; there is not a story-telling gene that determines whether or not you can do it, it's an ability that you cultivate through practice. There are stories everywhere—in the history and fiction you read in books, in Reader's Digest and the daily newspaper, from your own family. Use your imagination to adapt these stories to encourage the people you know and work with to be their best. Join Toastmasters or take a Dale Carnegie class to polish your skills at telling those stories. It's the single-best investment you can make in your leadership effectiveness.

Real leaders don't tolerate toxic negativity

You can't really encourage people in an organization where negative attitudes and demeaning behaviors are tolerated. The culture of any organization is determined by two things: what leaders *expect* and what they *tolerate*, and over time what you tolerate will dominate what you say you expect. It is incumbent upon leaders to do everything possible to create an environment that honors human dignity, irrespective of each individual's race, occupation, or social status, for two reasons. First, it is good business sense. In today's competitive world, you need the best thinking of all your people, and people think best when they're treated as equals. Second, it's a matter of integrity; the very word implies a wholeness and unity that is violated by prejudice and demeaning treatment. Create an environment in which everyone is treated with respect and dignity.

Proceed until apprehended!

When they see something that needs to be done, leaders don't wait for someone else to give them permission; they take the initiative, they take action, and if necessary they later ask forgiveness. Their philosophy is *proceed until apprehended.* They have taken to heart the seven simple promises of *The Self-Empowerment Pledge* with which we started this course, and empower themselves to do what needs to be done. In *The Analects*, Confucius said: *"to see what is right and not to do it is cowardice."* For the values-based leader, this is a great formula for encouraging others—help them see what is right, and then inspire them with the courage to do that which is right.

The I in team is U

You might have heard the phrase that there is no I in team. The point, of course, is that a team is no place for ego, self-interest, or personal aggrandizement to interfere with people working together. But looked at another way, their really *is* an I in team—in fact, more than one. Building a successful team begins with helping each member of that team (each "I") be the best that they can be. And that, of course, begins with the leader working to be the best that he or she can be.

 ## Rules for the Journey

1) Values-based leaders know that the ability to effectively communicate their values and their expectations is crucial to their effectiveness, so the work hard at developing these skills, including the essential talent of story-telling.

2) An important duty of leadership is to create an environment where people work together with a spirit of pride, collegiality, and friendship; you cannot effectively encourage people who are working in a toxic emotional environment.

3) The best leaders help people believe in themselves and in their dreams; they encourage people to bring their best to work with them, and to share their gifts and their passions with others.

4) When things go right, leaders give credit; when things go wrong, they take the blame.

5) Transforming leadership is ultimately and at its foundation spiritual leadership, encouraging people to connect with the higher purpose and greater meaning in their work.

 ## Take-home exercise: Make encouragement a way of life

Think about a time you were faced with a daunting challenge or had suffered a significant loss or setback, and someone's encouragement gave you the courage and the strength you needed to keep moving ahead. How did that encouragement make you feel? In what ways did it affect your performance? Now think of a time that you gave encouragement to someone else who was struggling. How do you think your encouragement made them feel? Did you help them find the courage and strength to carry on? How can these insights help you internalize a commitment to encourage others as a part of your daily awareness and routine? It is human nature to rise to the occasion during the darkest and most difficult of times, and to encourage those who are struggling with enormous problems. It is not quite so natural for us to make encouragement an ongoing expectation we hold of ourselves as leaders. For most of us, encouragement is like sunshine: we can live without it for a long time, but we're not nearly as pleasant or productive as we are with it.

Extra credit reading

"One of the most sacred relationships among teams of people is that between leaders and followers. This relationship, so central and crucial, depends to an extraordinary degree on the clearly expressed and consistently demonstrated values of the leader as seen through the special lens of followers. That is why leadership and ethics are inextricably woven together."

MAX DEPREE: *Leadership Jazz*

Something to think about

People will quit a job, but they will never quit a mission; people will leave an organization, but they will never leave a team; people will desert a boss, but they will never desert a leader.

Module #60
The Fourth Cornerstone of Leadership is Celebration

"The greatest of leaders, when the work his done, leaves the people saying to themselves, 'we did it ourselves'."

Our goal for this module

To realize that celebration is not a frivolous diversion from the real work, but is part and parcel of the real work, and that recognizing people for their accomplishments and helping them celebrate their victories is an essential element of values-based leadership.

Strains of the national anthem blend in with the clamorous applause from the stands. The glittering medal hangs heavy from the athlete's neck. This is it, the moment that culminates a lifetime of sacrifice, dedication and hard work. Tomorrow there will be new goals, but tonight is for celebration. Napoleon Bonaparte once marveled at the fact that a man will risk his life in battle for the chance to win a strip of colored ribbon. But that's the human story, isn't it? We all want to be recognized, to be made to feel special—and to celebrate our efforts, our successes, and even our failures. The enlightened leader appreciates the power of celebration. It is to an organization what an exclamation point is to a story, what a spark plug is to a car.

The paradox of parties

"Keep your eyes on the road, your nose to the grindstone, and your shoulder to the wheel—now try to get some work done" (anonymous). Southwest Airlines is the only airline that has been profitable for each of the past 30+ years, even as many of its rivals have gone through bankruptcy. Southwest has highest productivity in the industry. They have the highest morale in the industry, with more than 400 applicants for every job opening. How do they maintain *both* high productivity *and* high

morale? For one thing, they have more parties than the rest of the industry combined. At Southwest, they find any excuse for a celebration. And as they laugh and play their way through the workday, they've blown right past their "nose to the grindstone" competitors. You'll probably never see a book called *Party Your Way to the Top* on the *Business Week* bestseller list, but fostering a culture of celebration just might put your organization into the *Business Week* roster of the fastest-growing companies.

Celebrate away stress

I once conducted a series of presentations at a busy hospital where too few nurses were taking care of too many patients. I asked my audience to envision a situation where, at the end of a stress-filled shift, an ICU manager called food service to order root beer floats to be delivered STAT for the nurses about to go off duty, because she didn't want her people to take the accumulated stress and negativity home to dump on their families. An ICU manager from that hospital happened to be in my first group. She raised her hand and said that food service would never go along, giving her the excuse that root beer floats weren't in the budget. In the second group, the food service director remarked that if he received such a request from ICU, he would move heaven and earth to make it happen. How often do we miss out on such opportunities to show our people that we really care about them as people and not just hired hands, and to build bridges between different areas of the organization, because we don't make the time for celebration?

Celebrate both success and good faith failure

One day an engineer at Hewlett-Packard had a Eureka moment that solved one of his department's most pressing technical challenges. At a loss for something to immediately recognize the accomplishment, the engineer's boss reached into his desk and pulled out a banana. In the succeeding years, "the golden banana" became one of the most coveted awards given out for innovative accomplishments. At Mayo Medical Ventures, one of the most prestigious awards one can receive is the "Queasy Eagle." This is awarded for the most spectacularly failed investment as a way of reinforcing the fact that venture capital firms must encourage risk-taking (though people don't want to earn too many Queasy Eagles!). Recognition and celebration—ranging from golden bananas and queasy eagles to the company picnic—can have a highly positive cultural impact.

Reinforce culture with rituals

Think of rituals as being stories without words. Simple rituals can have a massive impact on culture if they are sustained over time. The early days of IBM were defined by men in blue suits and starched white shirts singing the IBM fight song; the early days of Wal-Mart were defined by Sam Walton leading employees in the Wal-Mart cheer. Today, the culture of the Texas Roadhouse steakhouse chain is shaped by "alley rallies" in which employees sing and cheer before heading out to line dance with customers. Rituals have always been an important way for humans to bring a sense of structure and purpose to their work, yet in today's organizations we're too busy for rituals (we've replaced them with meetings). What can you do to restore the spirit and practice of rituals? Not having the time is a poor excuse: the Texas Roadhouse alley rally takes less than two minutes.

Celebrating past accomplishments sets the stage for pursuing future accomplishments

When reading a book, most people finish one chapter before moving on to the next. That's a pretty good metaphor for our need to obtain closure on work of the past before moving too far ahead with work of the future. Celebration is the most effective way of closing out a chapter in a positive and fulfilling manner. It brings a sense of closure to old business—both the successes and the failures—and sets the stage for new ventures and new achievements.

 ## Rules for the Journey

1) Leaders foster teamwork, community, and a spirit of fellowship by celebrating personal and group achievements—and good faith failures.

2) According to the Gallup Organization, one of the most important determinants of whether employees are fully engaged in their work is if they have friends on the job. Effective leaders go out of their way to cultivate an empowering corporate culture and a positive and productive workplace environment.

3) Leaders take the time to celebrate both successes and good faith failures. If people are afraid of being punished for failure, you will eventually lose your

most creative and talented people. On the other hand, when you have a reputation for standing behind the people even if they have failed spectacularly (and yes, for celebrating those good faith failures), you will attract more creative and daring people, and keep the ones you have.

4) Rituals have always been an important way for humans to bring a sense of structure and purpose to their work, yet in today's workplace we're too busy for rituals (we've replaced them with meetings). What can you do to restore the spirit and practice of rituals in your organization?

5) *"Drive fear out of the workplace"* is one of the 14 points for total quality management developed by TQM guru W. Edwards Deming; real leaders don't drive people with fear, they inspire, the encourage, they guide, and they celebrate.

6) Capitalize on every opportunity to congratulate a coworker, celebrate a success (or a good attempt), and to astonish a customer. Spontaneity is not impulsivity—it is responding with joy to the surprises and delights of life, not thoughtlessly reacting to inner emotional conditions.

 ## Take-home exercise: Plan for a year of celebrations

Make a list of goals and wishes you have for the year to come, both at work and at home (if you've already made such a list, pull it out of the drawer). For each goal or wish, think about all of the people who will need to be involved in order for you to accomplish it. Now, for each goal imagine a suitable celebration. You might have a different celebration depending upon whether, or the degree to which, you were successful (or unsuccessful), but plan a celebration nonetheless. Visualize the celebration as it unfolds—the remarks you will make to the people who helped you along the way, the cutting of cake or popping of champagne bottle corks, the little gifts you will give to people at just the right moment. This does not have to be a big undertaking—in fact, since you're going to be doing a lot of them, it's probably best that it's not. Winston Churchill once said that it took him twenty minutes to prepare for an impromptu remark. Planning for lots of little impromptu celebrations is the mark of a wise leader.

Extra credit reading

"Leaders energize organizations by allowing their own naturalenthusiasmtoemergeandbysharingtheirstrong convictions about what might be, should be, and could be (if everyone's effort and commitment were engaged). There is an undeniable element of cheerleading in this... In light of this, it is odd to find so many leaders who try to suppress their own enthusiasm in order to appear cool, unengaged, and 'above' optimism and eagerness. Leaders can show enthusiasm in many different ways, but what is important is that it be authentic and not be hidden (and when there is no well-spring of natural enthusiasm to tap, that's probably a sign that they are doing the wrong thing)."

JAMES O'TOOLE: *Leadership A to Z*

Something to think about

Celebrations are the exclamation points of life—they punctuate the greatest lines of our stories.

Conclusion

See one, do one, teach one

If you hang around a surgery residency training program long enough, you'll eventually hear someone say this: *"See one, do one, teach one."* That aphorism conveys two important points. First, it implies that there's an awful lot to learn, so surgery residents can't waste time on their lessons but need to progress quickly from learning to doing to teaching. Second, it says that the best way to make sure you've really learned something is to teach it.

Now that you have worked your way through this course on *The Twelve Core Action Values*, you have "seen one." Hopefully you've already started putting what you've learned into practice, and will continue to do so—you are "doing one." Now, the best way for you to make sure that you make the most of this course is for you to share what you have learned with others—at home, at work, and in your community. In other words, "teach one."

As we conclude our journey through *The Twelve Core Action Values*, I'll leave you with this recommendation:

 **"Define your future by your dreams and not by your memories, by your hopes and not by your fears."**

CPSIA information can be obtained at www.ICGtesting.com
Printed in the USA
BVOW06s1339110315

391233BV00001B/5/P

9 781887 511261